Phil Keshavorzi

S0-ALE-820

Tuning of Industrial Control Systems

*An Independent Learning Module
from the
Instrument Society of America*

TUNING OF INDUSTRIAL CONTROL SYSTEMS

By Armando B. Corripio

INSTRUMENT SOCIETY OF AMERICA

Copyright© Instrument Society of America 1990

All rights reserved

Printed in the United States of America

In preparing this work, the author and publisher have not investigated or considered patents which may apply to the subject matter hereof. It is the responsibility of the readers and users of the subject matter to protect themselves against liability for infringement of patents. The information contained herein is of a general educational nature. Accordingly, the author and publisher assume no responsibility and disclaim all liability of any kind, however arising, as a result of using the subject matter of this work.

The equipment referenced in this work has been selected by the author as examples of the technology. No endorsement of any product is intended by the author or publisher. In all instances, the manufacturer's procedures should prevail regarding the use of specific equipment. No representation, expressed or implied, is made with regard to the availability of any equipment, process, formula, or other procedures contained herein.

No part of this publication may be reproduced, stored in a retrieval system, or transmitted, in any form or by any means, electronic, mechanical, photocopying, recording or otherwise, without the prior written permission of the publisher.

INSTRUMENT SOCIETY OF AMERICA
67 Alexander Drive
P.O. Box 12277
Research Triangle Park
North Carolina 27709

Library of Congress Cataloging-in-Publication Data

Corripio, Armando B.
    Tuning of industrial control systems / by Armando B. Corripio.
        p.   cm.
    Includes bibliographical references and index.
    ISBN 1-55617-233-8
    1. Process control—Automation.   2. Feedback control systems.   I. Title.
TS156.8.C678   1990
670.42'75—dc20   90-4653
                                                   CIP

ISBN 1-55617-233-8

TABLE OF CONTENTS

ISA's Independent Learning Modules

This book is an Independent Learning Module (ILM) as developed and published by the Instrument Society of America. The ILMs are the principal components of a major educational system designed primarily for independent self-study. This comprehensive learning system has been custom-designed and created for ISA to more fully educate people in the basic theories and technologies associated with applied instrumentation and control.

The ILM System is divided into several distinct sets of Modules on closely related topics; such a set of individually related Modules is called a Series. The ILM System is composed of:

- The ISA Series of Modules on Control Principles and Techniques
- The ISA Series of Modules on Fundamental Instrumentation
- The ISA Series of Modules on Unit Process and Unit Operation Control
- The ISA Series of Modules for Professional Development

The principal components of the Series are the individual ILMs (or Modules) such as this one. They are especially designed for independent self-study; no other text or references are required. The unique format, style, and teaching techniques employed in the ILMs make them a powerful addition to any library.

The ILMs published to date are:

Fundamentals of Process Control Theory—Paul W. Murrill—1981

Controlling Multivariable Processes—F. G. Shinskey—1981

Microprocessors in Industrial Control—Robert J. Bibbero—1982

Measurement and Control of Liquid Level—Chun H. Cho—1982

Control Valve Selection and Sizing—Les Driskell—1983

Fundamentals of Flow Measurement—Joseph P. DeCarlo—1984

Intrinsic Safety—E. C. Magison—1984

Digital Control—Theodore J. Williams—1984

pH Control—Gregory K. McMillan—1985

FORTRAN Programming—James M. Pruett—1986

Introduction to Telemetry—O. J. Strock—1987

Application Concepts in Process Control—Paul W. Murrill—1988

Controlling Centrifugal Compressors—Ralph Moore—1989

CIM in the Process Industries—John Bernard—1989

Continuous Control Techniques for Distributive Control Systems—Gregory K. McMillan—1989

Tuning of Industrial Control Systems—Armando B. Corripio—1990

Most of the original ILMs were envisioned to be the more traditional or fundamental subjects in instrumentation and process control. Clearly, with the publications planned over the next few years, the ILM Series will become much more involved in emerging technologies.

Recently, ISA has increased its commitment to the ILM Series and has set for itself a goal of publishing four ILMs each year. Obviously, this growing Series is part of a foundation for any professional library in instrumentation and control. The individual practitioner will find them of value, of course, and they are a necessity in any institutional or corporate library.

There is obvious value in maintaining continuity within your personal set of ILMs; place a standing purchase order with ISA.

Paul W. Murrill
ILM Consulting Editor

Comments About this Volume

This ILM is designed to expose you to the techniques of tuning industrial control systems. As are all other ILMs, it is written so that you can study it on your own. Although it is written from a practical rather than a theoretical point of view, the material is organized in each unit in a logical sequence so that you can easily see the reasons for the techniques that are presented.

Tuning is an important phase of the implementation of automatic control systems. The best control strategies will perform poorly if they are poorly tuned. The most important point to be made in this ILM is that tuning is an approximate rather than a precise procedure. In other words, it is not necessary to know the tuning parameters to three significant figures; most of the time two or even one significant figure is sufficient. In short, "tune coarse, not fine" is an important slogan in this course.

A complete guide to the ILM is given in Unit 1. The BASIC program listed in Appendix B, called DISCLOOP, has been found to be very useful for tuning computer control algorithms and for evaluating such features as dead time compensation.

Acknowledgments

The manuscript for this ILM has been prepared completely by one person and his word processor—although not always in complete cooperation with each other—but I must acknowledge the inspiration and encouragement of Dr. Paul Murrill, the ILM Consulting Editor, without whose help I would have given up many times along the way. I would like also to acknowledge the help of many of my students at LSU, graduate and undergraduate, for helping me learn along with them about process dynamics and control theory. In particular, Richard Balhoff, Steve Hunter, Shaoyu Lin, Dan Logue, Jacob Martin, Jr., Samuel Peebles, Carl Thomas, and Terrel Touchstone.

Many of the practical tips I have included in this ILM are drawn from my experiences at EXXON Chemical America's Baton Rouge Chemical Plant; among the people I would like to acknowledge there are Don Fowler, Raju Hajare, Dave Landry, Jack Nylin, and Doug White.

Armando B. Corripio

Unit 1:
Introduction and Overview

UNIT 1

Introduction and Overview

Welcome to ISA's Independent Learning Module *Tuning Techniques for Industrial Control Systems*. The first unit of this self-study program provides the information needed to take the course.

Learning Objectives — When you have completed this unit, you should:

A. Understand the general organization of the course.
B. Know the course objectives.
C. Know how to proceed through the course.

1-1. Course Coverage

This is an ILM on the fundamental techniques for tuning industrial control systems. It covers:

A. The common techniques for representing and measuring the dynamic characteristics of the controlled process.
B. The selection and tuning of the various modes of feedback control, including those of computer- and microprocessor-based controllers.
C. The selection and tuning of advanced control techniques: cascade, feedforward, multivariable, and adaptive control.

The course will focus on how the tuning methods relate to the dynamic characteristics of the controlled process. This approach will provide insight on the tuning procedures rather than a series of recipes to be memorized.

Given the widespread use of microprocessor- and computer-based controllers, techniques that were originally developed for analog instruments will be extended to digital controllers. Tuning techniques that have been specifically developed for digital controllers will be examined, as will adaptive and autotuning controllers.

No attempt is made in this ILM to be exhaustive in the presentation of tuning techniques. In fact, techniques based on frequency response, root locus, and state space analysis have been specifically omitted, because those techniques are more applicable to electrical and aerospace systems than to industrial processes. The nonlinear nature of industrial systems and the presence of transportation lag (dead time or time delay) is what makes those techniques unsuitable for tuning industrial control systems.

1-2. Purpose

The purpose of this ILM is to present, in easily understood terms, the principles and the practice of industrial controller tuning. Although the course cannot substitute for actual field experience, it is designed to provide insight into the tuning problem to speed up the learning process during field training.

1-3. Audience and Prerequisites

The material in this ILM will be useful to engineers, first-line supervisors, and senior technicians who are concerned with the design, installation, and operation of process control systems. The course will also be helpful to students in technical schools, colleges, or universities who wish to gain some insight into the practical aspects of automatic controller tuning.

There are no specific prerequisites to this course. However, it would be helpful to have some familiarity with the basic concepts of automatic process control, whether acquired from practical experience or academic study. In terms of mathematical skills, it is not necessary for the student to be intimately familiar with the mathematics used in the presentation in order to understand the fundamentals of tuning. It is hoped that the barrier that mathematics usually presents to the understanding of automatic control concepts will be kept to a minimum in this ILM.

1-4. Study Materials

This textbook is the only study material required in this course; it is one of ISA's ILM System. It is an independent, stand-alone textbook that is uniquely and specifically designed for self-study.

Contained in Appendix A is a list of suggested readings to provide additional reference and study materials for the student. The student will also find it useful to study the other ILMs that are available from ISA, which present a broad range of specific applications of instrumentation and process control techniques.

1-5. Organization and Sequence

This ILM is organized in ten separate units. The next three units (Units 2 through 4) are designed to teach the fundamental concepts of tuning, namely, the modes of feedback control, the characterization and measurement of process dynamic response, the selection of controller performance, and the adjustment of the tuning parameters. Unit 5 tells how to select controller modes and tuning parameters for some typical control loops. An entire unit, Unit 6, is devoted to the specific problem of tuning computer- and microprocessor-based control algorithms. The last four units, Units 7 through 10, demonstrate how to tune the more advanced industrial control strategies, namely, cascade, feedforward, multivariable, and adaptive control systems.

As is the case with other ILMs, the method of instruction used in this ILM is self-study. You select the pace at which you learn best. You may completely skip or browse through some units with which you feel you are intimately familiar and devote more time to other units that contain material new to you.

Each unit is designed in a consistent format with a set of specific *learning objectives* stated at the very beginning of the unit. Note these learning objectives carefully; the material in the unit will teach to these objectives. Each unit contains examples to illustrate specific concepts and exercises to test your understanding of these concepts. All of these exercises have solutions contained in Appendix C, against which you should check your solution.

You are encouraged to make notes in this textbook, taking advantage of the ample white space, which is provided on every page for this specific purpose.

1-6. Course Objectives

When you have completed this entire ILM, you should:

- Know how to characterize the dynamic response of an industrial process.
- Be able to measure the dynamic parameters of a process.
- Be able to select performance criteria and tune feedback controllers.
- Be able to pick the right controller modes and tuning parameters that match the objectives of the control system.
- Understand the effect of sampling frequency on the performance of computer-based controllers.
- Know when to apply and how to tune cascade, feedforward, ratio, and multivariable control systems.
- Be able to apply adaptive and autotuning control techniques to compensate for process nonlinearities.

Besides these overall course objectives, each individual unit contains its own set of learning objectives. These objectives are to help direct your study.

1-7. Course Length

The basic premise of ISA's ILM System is that students learn best when they proceed at their own pace. As a result, there will be a significant variation in the amount of time taken by individual students to complete this ILM. On the average, most students will complete this course in 30 to 40 hours, but individual experience and personal capabilities will do much to vary this time estimate.

Unit 2:
Feedback Controllers

UNIT 2

Feedback Controllers

This unit introduces the basic modes of feedback control, the important concept of control loop stability, and the ultimate gain method for tuning controllers.

Learning Objectives — When you have completed this unit you should:

A. Understand the concept of feedback control and describe the three basic controller modes: proportional, reset or integral, and rate or derivative.

B. Have an appreciation of what is meant by control loop stability, ultimate loop gain, and ultimate period.

C. Be able to tune simple feedback control loops with a minimum amount of information about the process.

2-1. The Feedback Control Loop

The earliest known industrial application of automatic control was the flywheel governor. This was a simple feedback controller, adapted by James Watt in 1775 for controlling the speed of a steam engine in the presence of varying loads. The concept had been used earlier to control the speed of windmills. In order to better understand the concept of feedback control, consider, as an example, the steam heater sketched in Fig. 2-1.

The process fluid flows inside the tubes of the heater and is heated by steam condensing on the outside of the tubes. The objective is to control the outlet temperature, C, of the process fluid in the presence of variations in process fluid flow (throughput or load), F, and in its inlet temperature, T_i. This is done by manipulating or adjusting the steam rate to the heater and with it the rate at which heat is transferred into the process fluid, thus affecting its outlet temperature.

In this example, the outlet temperature is the controlled (or output) variable, the steam flow is the manipulated variable, and the process fluid flow and inlet temperature are the disturbances. These terms are the standard terms recommended by the Instrument Society of America (ISA) to

9

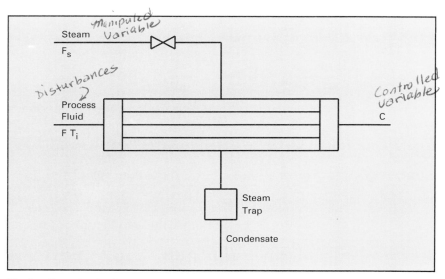

Fig. 2-1. Example of a Controlled Process: A Steam Heater.

refer to variables in a control system. They will be used throughout this ILM. *(independent Learning module)*

Now that the control objective and the important variables of the control system have been defined, the next step is deciding how to go about controlling the temperature. This can be accomplished by setting up a feedback control loop, which is the most common industrial control technique; in fact, it is the "bread and butter" of industrial automatic control. The concept of feedback control is as follows:

> Measure the controlled variable, compare it with its desired value, and adjust the manipulated variable based on the difference between the two.

The desired value of the controlled variable is the set point, and the difference between the controlled variable and the set point is the error.

In order to implement the feedback control scheme, three pieces of instrumentation are needed, as shown in Fig. 2-2:

1. A control valve for manipulating the steam flow.
2. A feedback controller for comparing the controlled variable with the set point and calculating the signal to the control valve.
3. A sensor/transmitter for measuring the controlled variable and transmitting a proportional signal to the controller.

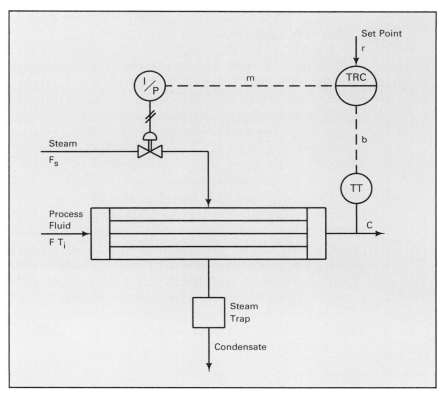

Fig. 2-2. Feedback Control Loop for Heater Outlet Temperature.

The controller and the sensor/transmitter are typically electronic (as indicated in Fig. 2-2) or pneumatic. In the former case the signals are electric currents in the range of 4-20 mA (milliamperes), while in the latter they are air pressure signals in the range of 3-15 psig (pounds per square inch gage). The control valve is usually pneumatically operated, requiring that the electric current signal from the controller be converted to an air pressure signal. This is done by a current-to-pressure transducer, labeled "I/P" in Fig. 2-2. The I/P is a one-to-one repeater that has no effect on the relative value of the signal in terms of its fraction or percent of range.

It can be seen in Fig. 2-2 that the feedback control scheme creates a loop around which signals travel: a change in outlet temperature, C, causes a proportional change in the signal to the controller, b, and therefore an error, e; the controller acts on this error by changing the signal to the control valve, m, causing a change in steam flow to the heater, F_s; this causes a change in the outlet temperature, C, which then starts a new cycle of changes around the loop.

The control loop and its various components are easier to recognize when represented as a block diagram, as shown in Fig. 2-3. Block diagrams were introduced by James Watt, who recognized that the complex workings of the linkages and levers of the flywheel governor are easier to explain and understand if they are considered as signal processing blocks and comparators. The basic elements of a block diagram are arrows, blocks (rectangles), and comparators (circles). The arrows represent the instrument signals and process variables (e.g., transmitter and controller output signals, steam flow, outlet temperature, etc.). The blocks represent the processing of the signals by the instruments and the lags, delays, and magnitude changes of the variables caused by the process and other pieces of equipment (e.g., the control valve, the sensor/transmitter, the controller and the heater). Finally, the comparators represent the addition and/or subtraction of signals (e.g., the calculation of the error signal in the controller).

The signs in the diagram represent the actions of the various input signals on the output signal; that is, a positive sign means that an increase in input causes an increase in output (direct action), while a negative sign means that an increase in input causes a decrease in output (reverse action). For example, the negative sign by the process flow into the heater means that an increase in flow results in a decrease in outlet temperature. Notice, by following the signals around the loop, that there is a net reverse action in the loop. This property is

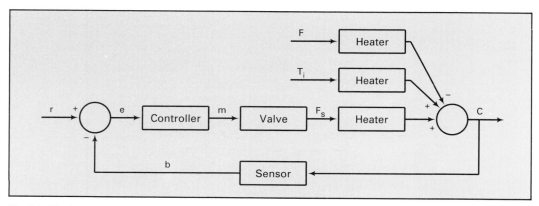

Fig. 2-3. Block Diagram of Feedback Control Loop.

known as negative feedback and, as will be seen shortly, is required for the loop to be stable.

Now that the various components of a feedback control loop have been defined, the most important one, the feedback controller, will be examined.

2-2. Proportional, Integral, and Derivative Modes

As stated in the previous section, the purpose of the feedback controller is twofold: first, it computes the error as the difference between the controlled variable and the set point; second, it computes the signal to the control valve based on the error. This section presents the various ways or "modes" used by the controller to perform the second of these two functions. In the next section these modes are combined to form the feedback controllers most commonly used in industry.

The three basic modes of feedback control are proportional, integral (or reset), and derivative (or rate). Each of these modes introduces an adjustable or tuning parameter into the operation of the feedback controller. The controller can consist of a single mode, a combination of two modes, or a combination of all three.

The purpose of the proportional mode is to cause an instantaneous response of the controller output to changes in the error. The formula for the proportional mode is:

$$K_c e \tag{2-1}$$

where K_c is the controller gain and e is the error. The significance of the controller gain is that the larger it is, the larger the change in the controller output caused by a given error. This is illustrated in Fig. 2-4, where the response in the controller output due to the proportional mode is shown for a step change in error at various values of the gain.

Another way of looking at the gain is that the larger it is, the smaller the change in error that causes a full scale change in the controller output signal. This allows the gain to be expressed as the proportional band (PB), which is the change in the transmitter signal (expressed as percent of its range) that is required to cause a 100% change in controller output.

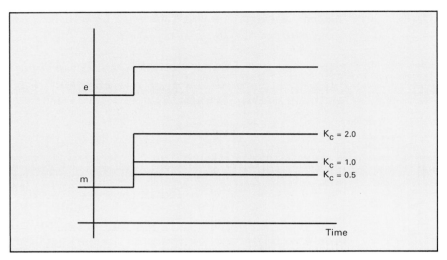

Fig. 2-4. Response of Proportional Controller to Constant Error.

The relationship between the controller gain and its proportional band is then given by the following formula:

$$PB = \frac{100}{K_c} \quad \text{Controller gain}$$ (2-2)

Some instrument manufacturers calibrate the controller gain as proportional band, while others do it as gain. It is very important to realize that increasing the gain reduces the proportional band and vice versa.

The proportional mode cannot by itself eliminate the error at steady state in the presence of disturbances and changes in set point. The unavoidability of this permanent error or offset can best be understood by considering the steam heater control loop of Fig. 2-2 with a controller that has proportional-only mode. The formula for such a controller is:

$$m = m_0 + K_c e \quad \text{bias}$$ (2-3)

where m is the controller output signal and m_0 is its bias or base value. This base value is usually adjusted at calibration time at about 50% of the controller output range to give the controller room to move in each direction; however, assume that the bias on the temperature controller of this steam heater has been adjusted to produce zero error at the normal operating conditions; that is, the steam control valve has been positioned so that the steam flow is that which will produce the desired outlet temperature at the normal process flow and inlet temperature.

The response of the outlet temperature and of the controller output to a step change in process flow is shown in Fig. 2-5 for the case of no control and for two different values of the proportional gain. For the case of no control, the steam rate remains the same, causing the temperature to drop because there is more fluid to heat with the same amount of heat. The proportional controller can reduce this error by opening the steam valve, as shown in Fig. 2-5, but it cannot eliminate it completely because, as can be seen from Eq. (2-3), zero error results in the original steam valve position, which is not enough steam rate to bring the temperature back up to its desired value. Although an increased controller gain results in a smaller steady-state error or offset, it also causes, as shown in Fig. 2-5, oscillations in the response. This is caused by the time delays on the signals as they travel around the loop and overcorrection by the controller as the gain is increased. In order to eliminate the offset, a control mode other than proportional is needed, that is, the integral mode.

The purpose of the integral or reset mode is to eliminate the offset or steady-state error. It does this by integrating or

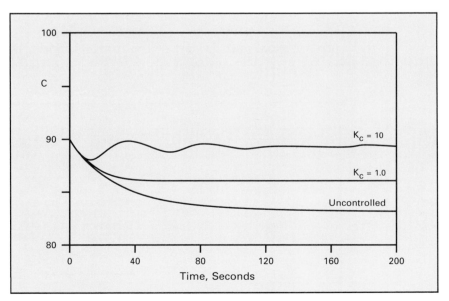

Fig. 2-5. Response of Heater Temperature to Step Change in Process Flow Using a Proportional Controller.

accumulating the error over time. The formula for the integral mode is:

$$\frac{K_c}{T_I} \int edt \qquad (2\text{-}4)$$

where t is time and T_I is the integral or reset time. The calculus operation of integration is somewhat difficult to visualize; perhaps it is best understood through a physical analogy. Consider the tank shown in Fig. 2-6 and assume that the liquid level in the tank represents the output of the integral action, while the difference between the inlet and outlet flow rates represents the error e. When the inlet flow rate is higher than that of the outlet, the error is positive and the level rises with time at a rate that is proportional to the error. Conversely, if the outlet flow rate is higher, the level drops at a rate proportional to the negative error. Finally, the only way for the level to remain stationary is for the inlet and outlet flows to be equal, in which case the error is zero. The integral mode of the feedback controller acts exactly in this manner, thus fulfilling its purpose of forcing the error to zero at steady state.

The integral time T_I is the tuning parameter of the integral mode. In the analogous tank of Fig. 2-6, the cross-sectional area of the tank represents the integral time. The smaller the integral time (area), the faster the controller output (level) will change for a given error (difference in flows). Since the proportional gain is part of the integral mode, the integral

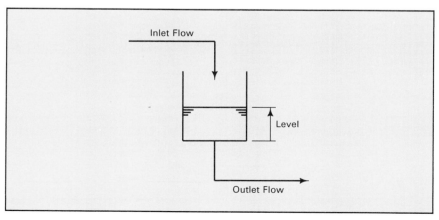

Fig. 2-6. Tank Analog of Integral Controller.

time is the time it takes for the integral mode to match the instantaneous change caused by the proportional mode on a step change in error. This concept is illustrated in Fig. 2-7. Some instrument manufacturers calibrate the integral mode parameter as the reset rate, which is simply the reciprocal of the integral time. Again, it is important to realize that increasing the integral time results in a decrease in the reset rate and vice versa.

Although the integral mode is effective in eliminating offset, it is slower than the proportional mode because it must act over a period of time. A faster mode than the proportional is the derivative mode.

The derivative or rate mode responds to the rate of change of the error with time. This speeds up the controller action, compensating for some of the delays in the feedback loop. The formula for the derivative action is:

$$K_c T_D \frac{de}{dt} \qquad (2\text{-}5)$$

where T_D is the derivative or rate time. Derivative time is the time it takes the proportional mode to match the instantaneous action of the derivative mode on an error that changes linearly with time (a ramp). This is illustrated in Fig. 2-8. Notice that the derivative mode acts only when the error is changing with time.

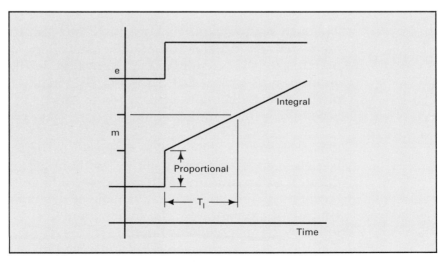

Fig. 2-7. Response of PI Controller to a Constant Error.

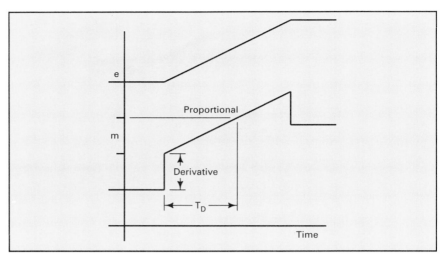

Fig. 2-8. Response of PD Controller to an Error Ramp.

The three basic modes of feedback control discussed thus far are all proportional to the error in their action; that is, a doubling in the magnitude of the error causes a doubling in the magnitude of the change in controller output. On-off control, in which the controller output switches from one end of its range to the other depending only on the sign of the error, not on its magnitude, has not been mentioned. On-off controllers are not generally used in process control, and, when they are, it is very simple to tune them. Their only adjustment is the magnitude of a dead band around the set point.

The next section explains how the three basic control modes are combined in industrial process controllers; but, first, the notation for the integral and derivative modes needs to be simplified. A look at Eqs. (2-4) and (2-5) makes this need obvious. Introducing the Heaviside operator ''s'' can accomplish this simplification.

Oliver Heaviside (1850–1925) was a British physicist who baffled mathematicians by noting, without proof, that the differentiation operator d/dt, called s, could be treated as an algebraic quantity. Taking advantage of this concept can simplify the notation for the integral and derivative modes as follows: the rate of change of the error is denoted by ''se,'' and the integration of the error is denoted by ''e/s.'' (The integration is the reciprocal operation because the rate of change of the output is proportional to the input.) This will allow the formulas for the integral and derivative modes to be written as:

Integral mode: $\dfrac{K_c}{T_I s}\, e$ (2-6)

Derivative mode: $K_c T_D s e$ (2-7)

These are simpler than Eqs. (2-4) and (2-5). (For those of you who are not comfortable with the mathematics, be assured that it is used only to simplify the explanations.) Nevertheless, it is important for you to begin associating the s operator with rate of change and its reciprocal with integration. It is also important to realize that since s is associated with rate of change, it takes on a value of zero (that is, it disappears) at steady state, when there is no change.

2-3. Typical Industrial Feedback Controllers

Approximately seventy-five percent of industrial feedback controllers are proportional-integral (PI) or two-mode controllers; most of the balance are proportional-integral-derivative (PID) or three-mode controllers. As Unit 5 will show, some applications require single-mode controllers—either proportional or integral—but these are few. It is also rather easy to tune a single-mode controller, as only one tuning parameter needs to be adjusted. This section presents PI and PID controllers in terms of how the modes are combined and implemented and will consider both the analog (electronic and pneumatic) and digital (microprocessor and computer) implementations of feedback controllers.

The formula for the PI controller results from the simple addition of the proportional and integral modes:

$$m = K_c\left[e + \frac{1}{T_I s}\, e\right]$$

$$= K_c\left[1 + \frac{1}{T_I s}\right] e \qquad (2\text{-}8)$$

Equation (2-8) shows that the PI controller has two adjustable parameters, the gain K_c and the integral time T_I. A block diagram representation of the PI controller is shown in Fig. 2-9.

The simplest formula for the PID or three-mode controller is the addition of the proportional, integral, and derivative modes:

$$m = K_c \left[1 + \frac{1}{T_I s} + T_D s \right] e \qquad (2\text{-}9)$$

This equation shows that the PID controller has three adjustable or tuning parameters: the gain K_c, the integral time T_I, and the derivative time T_D. The block diagram implementation of Eq. (2-9) is sketched in Fig. 2-10a. The alternative form, Fig. 2-10b, is more commonly used because it avoids taking the rate of change of the set point input to the controller, thus preventing the undesirable derivative "kick" on set point changes by the process operator.

The formula of Eq. (2-9) is commonly used in computer-based controllers, seen in more detail in Unit 6. It is referred to as the "parallel" PID controller because, as can be seen in Fig. 2-10, the three modes are in parallel. All analog and most microprocessor (distributed) controllers use a "series" PID controller, given by the following formula:

$$m = K_c' \left[\frac{1 + T_D' s}{1 + \alpha T_D' s} \right] \left[1 + \frac{1}{T_I' s} \right] e \qquad (2\text{-}10)$$

The first term in brackets is a derivative unit attached to the standard PI controller of Fig. 2-9 to create the PID controller

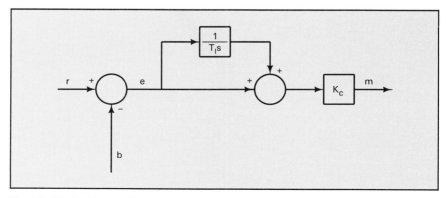

Fig. 2-9. Block Diagram of PI Controller.

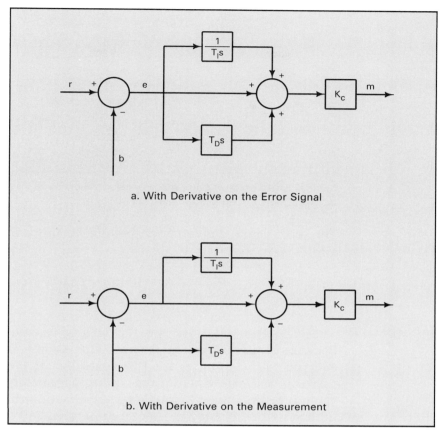

a. With Derivative on the Error Signal

b. With Derivative on the Measurement

Fig. 2-10. Block Diagrams of Parallel PID Controller.

shown in Fig. 2-11. It contains a filter (lag) to prevent the amplification of noise. The derivative unit is installed on the controlled variable input to the controller in order to avoid the derivative kick, just as in Fig. 2-10b. The value of the filter parameter α in Eq. (2-10) is not adjustable but is built into the design of the controller. It is usually of the order of 0.05 to 0.1. The noise filter can and should be added to the derivative term of the parallel version of the PID controller. Its effect on the response of the controller can be neglected.

The following formulas convert the parameters of the series PID controller to those of the parallel version:

$$F_{sp} = 1 + (T'_D/T'_I) \tag{2-11}$$

$$K_c = K'_c F_{sp} \qquad T_I = T'_I F_{sp} \qquad T_D = T'_D/F_{sp}$$

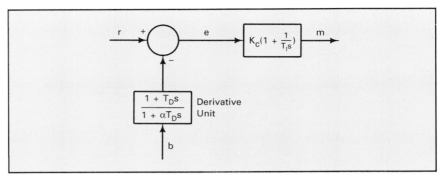

Fig. 2-11. Block Diagram of Series PID Controller with Derivative on the Measurement.

The formulas to convert from parallel to series PID parameters are:

$$F_{ps} = 0.5 + [0.25 - (T_D/T_I)]^{0.5} \qquad (2\text{-}12)$$

$$K'_c = K_c F_{ps} \qquad T'_I = T_I F_{ps} \qquad T'_D = T_D/F_{ps}$$

Because of this difference between the parameters of the series and parallel versions of the PID controller, this text will carefully indicate whether the tuning parameters are for one version or the other. Manuals for specific controllers will indicate whether they are series or parallel so that they can be properly tuned. Notice that there is no difference when the derivative time is zero (PI controller).

Some features are common to all controllers, whether they are electronic, pneumatic, or computer-based:

    Features Intended for the Plant Operator
        Controlled variable display
        Set point display
        Controller output signal display
        Set point adjustment
        Manual output adjustment
        Remote/local set point switch (cascade systems only)
        Auto/manual switch

    Features Intended for the Instrument or Control Engineer
        Proportional gain, integral time, and derivative time
            adjustments
        Direct/reverse action switch

The operator features are on the front of panel-mounted controllers or in the "menu" of the computer control video display screens. The instrument/control engineer features are on the side of panel-mounted controllers or in separate computer video screens that require a key or separate password to be accessed.

The most common forms of feedback controllers have been described; attention now will focus on loop stability, that is, the interaction between the controller and the process.

2-4. Stability of the Feedback Loop

One of the characteristics of feedback control loops is that they may become unstable. The loop is said to be unstable when a small change in disturbance or set point causes the system to deviate widely from its normal operating point. The two possible causes of instability are that the controller has the incorrect action or that it is tuned too tightly; that is, either the gain is too high, the integral time is too small, the derivative time is too high, or a combination of these. Another possible cause is that the process is inherently unstable, but this is rare.

When the controller has the incorrect action, instability is manifested by the controller output "running away" to either its upper or its lower limit. For example, if the temperature controller on the steam heater of Fig. 2-2 were set so that an increasing temperature would increase its output, a small increase in temperature would result in an opening of the steam valve, which, in turn, would increase the temperature more, and the cycle would continue until the controller output would be at its maximum with the steam valve fully opened. On the other hand, a small decrease in temperature would result in a closing of the steam valve, which would further reduce the temperature, and the cycle would continue until the controller output was at its minimum point with the steam valve fully closed. Thus, the stability of the temperature control loop of Fig. 2-2 requires that the controller action be "increasing measurement decreases output" (reverse).

When the controller is tuned too tightly, instability can be recognized by observing that the signals in the loop oscillate and the amplitude of the oscillations increase with time, as

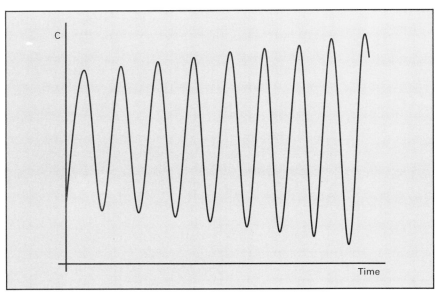

Fig. 2-12. Response of Unstable Feedback Control Loop.

illustrated in Fig. 2-12. The cause of this instability is that the tightly tuned controller overcorrects for the error, and, because of the delays and lags around the loop, the overcorrections are not detected by the controller until some time later, causing a larger error in the opposite direction and further overcorrection. If allowed to continue, the controller output will end up oscillating between its upper and lower limits.

As pointed out earlier, the oscillatory type of instability is caused by the controller having a too high gain, a too fast integral time, or a too high derivative time. This leads into the simplest method for characterizing the process for the purpose of tuning the controller: determining the ultimate gain and period of oscillation of the loop.

2-5. Determination of the Ultimate Gain and Period

The earliest published method of characterizing the process for controller tuning was proposed by J. G. Ziegler and N. B. Nichols around 1940. Their method consists of determining the ultimate gain and period of oscillation of the loop. The ultimate gain is defined as the gain of a proportional controller at which the loop oscillates with constant amplitude, and the ultimate period is the period of the oscillations. The ultimate gain is thus a measure of the controllability of the loop; that is, the higher the ultimate gain, the easier it is to control the loop. The ultimate period is, in turn, a measure of the speed of response of the loop; that is, the longer the period, the slower the loop.

By its definition it can be deduced that the ultimate gain is the gain at which the loop is at the threshold of instability. At gains just below the ultimate, the loop signals will oscillate with decreasing amplitude, as in Fig. 2-5; at gains above the ultimate, the amplitude of the oscillations will increase with time, as in Fig. 2-12. It is, therefore, very important when determining the ultimate gain of an actual feedback control loop to ensure that it is not exceeded by much, or the result would be a violently unstable system.

The procedure for determining the ultimate gain and period is carried out with the controller in "auto" and with the integral and derivative modes removed. It is as follows:

1. Remove the integral mode by setting the integral time to its highest value (or the reset rate to its lowest value.) Alternatively, if the controller model or program allows for switching off the integral mode, switch it off.
2. Switch off the derivative mode or set the derivative time to its lowest value, usually zero.
3. Carefully increase the proportional gain in steps. After each increase, disturb the loop by introducing a small step change in set point and observe the response of the controlled and manipulated variables, preferably on a trend recorder. The variables should start oscillating as the gain is increased, as in Fig. 2-5.
4. When the amplitude of the oscillations remains constant (or approximately constant) from one oscillation to the next, the ultimate controller gain has been reached. Record it as K_{cu}.
5. Measure the period of the oscillations from the trend recordings, as shown in Fig. 2-13, or with a stop watch. For better accuracy, time several oscillations and calculate the average period.
6. Stop the oscillations by reducing the gain to about half of the ultimate.

The procedure just outlined is simple and requires a minimum upset to the process, just enough to be able to observe the oscillations. Nevertheless, the prospect of taking a process

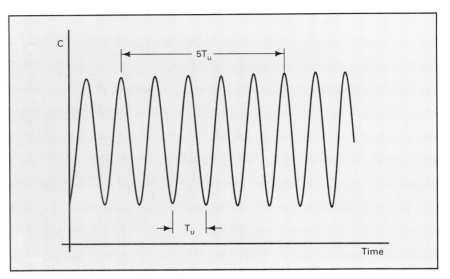

Fig. 2-13. Determination of Ultimate Period.

control loop to the verge of instability is not an attractive one from a process operation standpoint. However, it is not absolutely necessary in practice to obtain sustained oscillations (see below). It is also important to realize that some loops cannot be made to oscillate with constant amplitude with only a proportional controller. Fortunately, these are usually the simplest loops to control and tune.

2-6. Tuning for Quarter-Decay Response

Along with the method outlined in the preceding section for determining the ultimate gain and period of a feedback control loop, Ziegler and Nichols proposed that they be used in tuning the controller for a specific response: the quarter-decay ratio (QDR) response. The QDR response is illustrated in Fig. 2-14 for a step change in set point and for a step change in disturbance. Its characteristic is that each oscillation has an amplitude that is one fourth that of the previous oscillation. The formulas proposed by Ziegler and Nichols (1942) for calculating the QDR tuning parameters of P, PI, and PID controllers from the ultimate gain K_{cu} and period T_u are summarized in Table 2-1.

It is intuitively obvious that for the proportional (P) controller the gain for QDR response should be half the ultimate gain. At

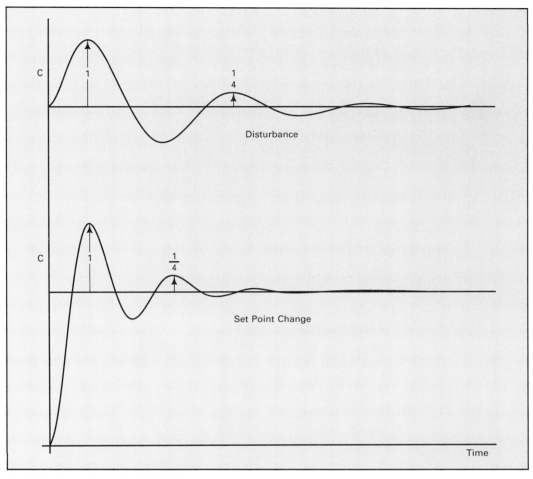

Fig. 2-14. Quarter-Decay Ratio (QDR) Responses.

the ultimate gain, the maximum error in each direction causes an identical maximum error in the opposite direction. At half the ultimate gain, the maximum error in each direction is exactly half the preceding maximum error in the opposite direction and one fourth the previous maximum error in the same direction. This is the quarter-decay response.

TABLE 2-1. QUARTER-DECAY RATIO TUNING FORMULAS

Controller	Gain	Integral Time	Derivative Time
P	$K_c = 0.5\ K_{cu}$	—	—
PI	$K_c = 0.45\ K_{cu}$	$T_I = T_u/1.2$	—
PID, series	$K_c = 0.6\ K_{cu}$	$T_I = T_u/2$	$T_D = T_u/8$
PID, parall.	$K_c = 0.75\ K_{cu}$	$T_I = T_u/1.6$	$T_D = T_u/10$

Notice that the addition of integral mode results in a reduction of 10% in the QDR gain between the P and the PI controller tuning formulas. This is due to the additional lag introduced by the integral mode. On the other hand, the addition of the derivative mode allows increasing the controller gain by 20% over the proportional-only controller. Therein lies the justification for the derivative mode, that is, the increase in the controllability of the loop. Finally, the derivative and integral times in the series PID controller formulas are in the ratio of $1:4$. This is a useful relationship to remember when tuning PID controllers by trial and error because the ultimate gain and period can not be determined.

Example 2-1, Ultimate Gain Tuning of Steam Heater:
Determine the ultimate gain and period for the temperature control loop of Fig. 2-2, and the quarter-decay tuning parameters for P, PI, and PID controllers.

Figure 2-15 shows the determination of the ultimate gain for the temperature control loop. A 2°C change in set point is used to start the oscillations. The figure shows responses for the proportional controller with gains of 8 and 12%/%. The latter is the ultimate gain:

Ultimate gain: 12%/% (8.33% PB)

Ultimate period: 0.60 minute

Using the formulas from Table 2-1, the QDR tuning parameters are:

P controller: Gain = 0.5 (12)   = 6.0%/% (17% PB)
PI controller: Gain = 0.45 (12)   = 5.4%/% (18% PB)
                 T_I = 0.60/1.2   = 0.50 minute

Series PID   Gain = 0.6 (12) = 7.2%/% (14% PB)
  controller:
                   T_I' = 0.60/2   = 0.30 minute

                   T_D' = 0.60/8   = 0.075 minute

Figure 2-16 shows the response of the controller output and the outlet process temperature to a 5°C change in set point for the proportional controller with the QDR gain of 6%/% and with half that gain. Similarly, Figs. 2-17 and 2-18 show the responses of the PI and series PID controllers, respectively. In

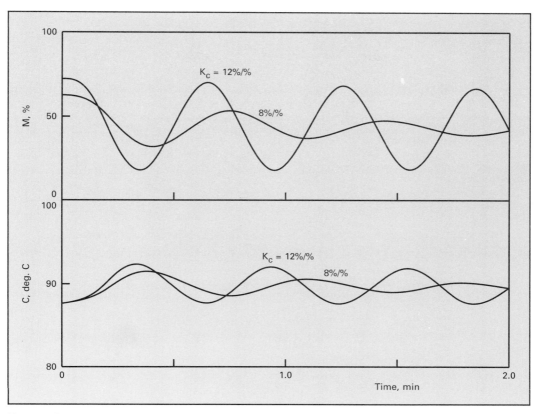

Fig. 2-15. Determination of Ultimate Gain and Period for Temperature Control Loop on Steam Heater.

each case, the reduction of the proportional gain results in a less oscillatory behavior and less initial movement of the controller output, at the expense of a slightly slower approach to the new set point. This shows that the tuning parameters, particularly the gain, can be varied from the values given by the formulas.

Notice the offset in Fig. 2-16 and the significant improvement that the derivative mode produces in the responses of Fig. 2-18 over those of Fig. 2-17.

Practical Ultimate Gain Tuning Tips

1. In determining the ultimate gain and period, it is not absolutely necessary to force the loop to oscillate with constant amplitude, because the ultimate period does not vary drastically as the loop approaches the ultimate gain. Any oscillation that would allow a rough estimate of the

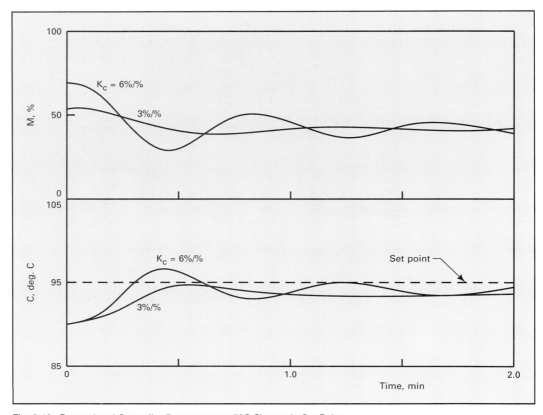

Fig. 2-16. Proportional Controller Response to a 5°C Change in Set Point.

ultimate period gives good enough values of the integral and derivative times. Then the proportional gain can be adjusted to obtain an acceptable response. For example, notice in Fig. 2-15 that, for the case of a gain of 8%/%, the period of oscillation is 0.7 minute, which is only about 15% off from the actual ultimate period.

2. The performance of the feedback controller is not usually sensitive to the tuning parameters. Thus, when adjusting the parameters from the values given by the formulas, it is usually a waste of time to change them by less than 50%.

3. The recommended parameter adjustment policy is to leave the integral and derivative times fixed at the values calculated from the tuning formulas and adjust the gain, up or down, to obtain the desired response.

The QDR tuning formulas allow tuning controllers for a specific response when the ultimate gain and period of the loop are known. In the units that follow are alternative

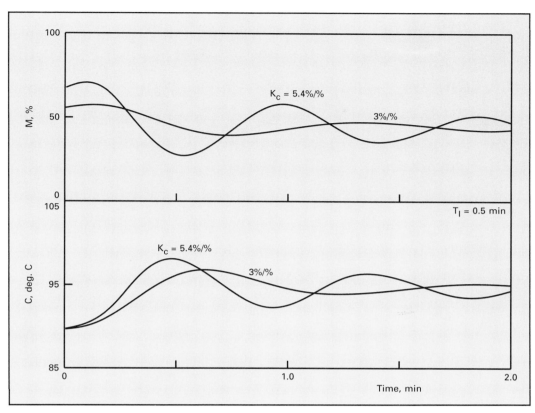

Fig. 2-17. Proportional-Integral (PI) Controller Response to a 5°C Change in Set Point (T_I = 0.5 minute).

methods for characterizing the dynamic response of the loop and for tuning feedback controllers. The following section brings up the need for such alternative methods.

2-7. Need for Alternatives to Ultimate Gain Tuning

Although the ultimate gain tuning method is simple and fast, other methods of characterizing the dynamic response of feedback control loops have been developed over the years. The need for these alternative methods is based on the fact that it is not always possible to determine the ultimate gain and period of a loop. As pointed out earlier, some simple loops would not exhibit constant amplitude oscillations with a proportional controller.

The ultimate gain and period, although sufficient to tune most loops, do not give insight into which process or control system characteristics could be modified to improve the

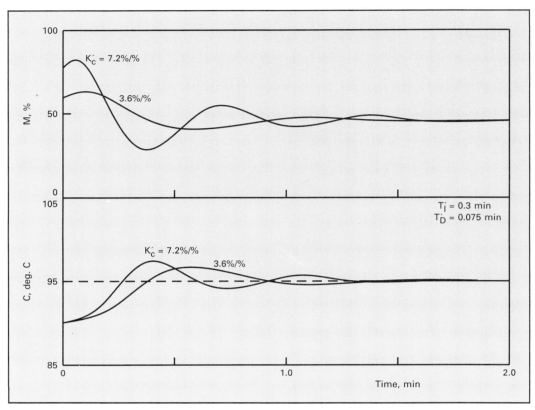

Fig. 2-18. Series PID Controller Response to a 5°C Change in Set Point (T$_I$ = 0.30 minute; T$_D$ = 0.075 minute).

feedback controller performance. A more fundamental method of characterizing process dynamics is needed to guide such modifications.

There is also the need to develop tuning formulas for responses other than the quarter-decay ratio response, because the PI and PID tuning parameters that produce quarter-decay response are not unique. It is obvious that for each setting of the integral and derivative times, there will usually be a setting of the controller gain that will produce quarter-decay response. This makes for an infinite number of combinations of the tuning parameters that will satisfy the quarter-decay specifications.

The next unit presents an open-loop method for characterizing the dynamic response of the process in the loop. The unit that follows will deal with alternative loop response specifications and the tuning formulas for attaining them.

2-8. Summary

This unit reviewed the concepts of feedback control, controller modes, and the stability of control loops. The concept of block diagrams was introduced. The ultimate gain method of tuning feedback controllers for quarter-decay ratio response was described and shown to be simple and fast but limited as to the fundamental insight it can provide on the performance of the feedback controller. Alternative process characterization and tuning methods will be presented in the units that follow.

Exercises

2-1. Consider Watt's steam engine controlled by a flywheel governor and driving the main shaft in a 19th-century machine shop. The various lathes, drills, etc., are driven by belts that are connected to the main shaft through manually operated clutches. Identify the controlled variable, the manipulated variable, and the disturbances for the engine speed controller. Identify also the sensor, and draw a block diagram for the feedback loop, identifying each block.

2-2. Repeat 2-1 for a conventional home oven. What variable does the cook vary when he or she adjusts the temperature dial?

2-3. How much does the output of a proportional controller change when the error changes by 5% if its gain is:
(a) 20% PB?   (b) 50% PB?   (c) 250% PB?

2-4. A proportional controller with a PB of 20% is used to control the temperature of the steam heater of Fig. 2-2. After an increase in process fluid flow, the heater reaches a new steady state in which the steam valve position has changed by 8%. What is the offset in the outlet temperature? What must be done to the steam valve to eliminate the offset—open it or close it? What would be the offset if the controller PB were 10% and all other conditions were the same?

2-5. In testing a PI controller, you set the proportional gain to 0.6 and the reset time to 2 minutes. Then you apply a sustained error of 5% and switch the controller to automatic. Describe quantitatively how the controller *output will respond with time and sketch the time response.*

2-6. *Repeat 2-5 for a PID controller with a gain of 1.0, a reset rate of 0 repeats per minute, and a derivative time of 2.0 minutes. In this case the error signal applied to the controller is as shown below, that is, a ramp of 5% per minute applied for 5 minutes.*

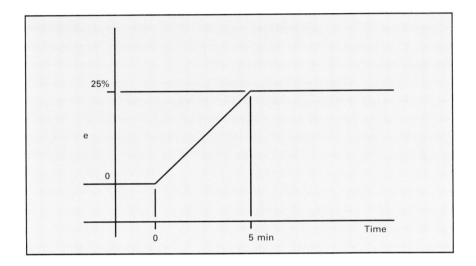

2-7. *A test is made on the temperature control loop for a fired heater. It is determined that the controller gain required to cause sustained oscillations is 1.2 and the period of the oscillations is 4.5 min. Determine the QDR tuning parameters for a PI controller. Report the controller gain as a proportional band and the reset rate in repeats per minute.*

2-8. *Repeat 2-7 for series and parallel PID controllers.*

Reference

Ziegler, J. G., and Nichols, N. B., "Optimum Settings for Automatic Controllers," *Transactions ASME*, V. 64 (Nov. 1942), p. 759.

Unit 3:
Open-Loop Characterization of Process Dynamics

UNIT 3

Open-Loop Characterization of Process Dynamics

This unit shows how to characterize the dynamic response of a process from open-loop step tests. Process gain, time constant, and dead time, which are the parameters needed to tune feedback and feedforward controllers in the units to follow, can be determined by the results of the step tests.

Learning Objectives — When you have completed this unit you should:

A. Know how to perform open-loop step tests and analyze the results of the tests.

B. Define process gain, time constant, and dead time, and know how to determine them for a process.

C. Appreciate the difficulties that the nonlinear nature of most processes impose on characterization and tuning.

D. Be able to determine dynamic parameters for both continuous and batch processes.

3-1. Open-Loop Testing—Why and How

The preceding unit showed how to determine the ultimate gain and period of a feedback control loop by performing a test with the controller on "automatic output," that is, with the loop closed. By contrast, this unit shows how to determine the process dynamic parameters by performing a test with the controller on "manual output," that is, an open-loop test. Such tests present a more fundamental model of the process than the ultimate gain and period.

The purpose of an open-loop test is to determine the transfer function of the process (the relationship between the process output variables and its input variables). In the case of a feedback control loop, the transfer function between the controlled or measured variable and the manipulated variable is of most interest. However, the transfer function between the controlled variable and a disturbance can also be determined, provided that the disturbance variable can be changed and measured. This unit is restricted to the manipulated/controlled variable pair, as the principles of the testing procedure and analysis are the same for any pair of variables.

To better understand the open-loop test concept, the block diagrams introduced in section 2-1 will be used. Consider the temperature feedback control loop of the heater sketched in Fig. 3-1. When the controller is switched to "manual output," the loop is interrupted at the controller and the controller output signal or manipulated variable, m, can be manually changed. Under these conditions, a block diagram showing the relationship between the manipulated and measured variables is shown in Fig. 3-2(a). It is convenient to combine the three blocks of Fig. 3-2(a) into the single block of Fig. 3-2(b), because this emphasizes the two signals of interest in an open-loop test, the controller output variable, m, and the transmitter output signal, b. Notice that the controlled variable, C, does not appear in the diagram of Fig. 3-2(b). This is because, in practice, the true process variable cannot be accessed; what is accessed is the measurement of that variable (the transmitter output signal b). Similarly, the flow through the control valve, F_s, does not appear explicitly in Fig. 3-2(b), because, even if it could be measured, the controller output signal, m, is of more interest, as this is the variable that is directly manipulated by the controller.

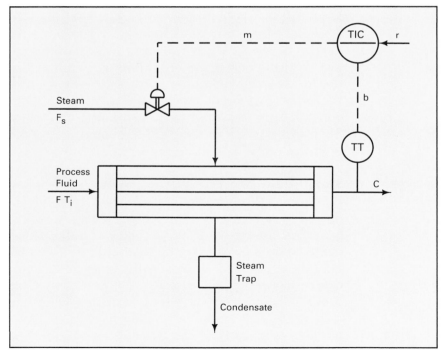

Fig. 3-1. Sketch of Temperature Control of Steam Heater.

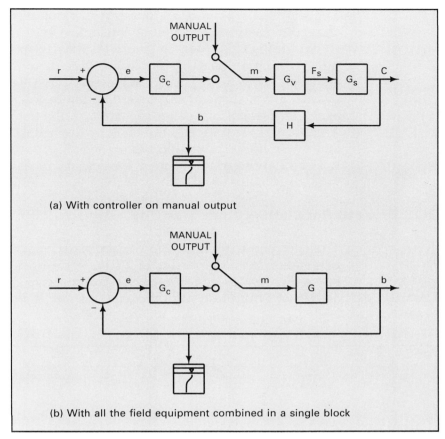

(a) With controller on manual output

(b) With all the field equipment combined in a single block

Fig. 3-2. **Block Diagram of Feedback Control Loop with Controller on Manual.**

The procedure for performing an open-loop test is simply to cause a step change in the process input, m, and record the resulting response of the transmitter signal, b. The equipment required to cause the change is simply the controller itself, given that its output can be controlled when it is in the manual state. The recording of the transmitter signal requires a trend recording device with variable chart speed and sensitivity. The regular trend recorders found in most control rooms are not appropriate because they are usually too slow and not sensitive enough to provide the precision required for the analysis of the test results. Computer- and microprocessor-based controllers are ideal for open-loop testing because they allow more precise change in their outputs than do their analog counterparts. The recording of the transmitter output can be done by storing the values sampled by the computer in its memory, in which case the trend recorder is not needed.

The simplest type of open-loop test is a step test (a step change in the process input signal, m). A typical step test is shown in Fig. 3-3. More accurate results can be obtained with pulse testing at the expense of considerably more involved analysis. Pulse testing will not be considered here because it is outside the scope of this text. The interested reader can find excellent discussions of pulse testing in the books listed in Appendix A, specifically the ones by Luyben (Reference 1) and by Smith and Corripio (Reference 3). Sinusoidal testing is not at all appropriate for most industrial processes because they are usually too slow.

3-2. Process Parameters from Step Test

The next phase is extracting the process characteristic parameters from the results of a step test. Consider the step test of Fig. 3-3 as an example. The parameters that can be estimated from the results of a step test are the process gain,

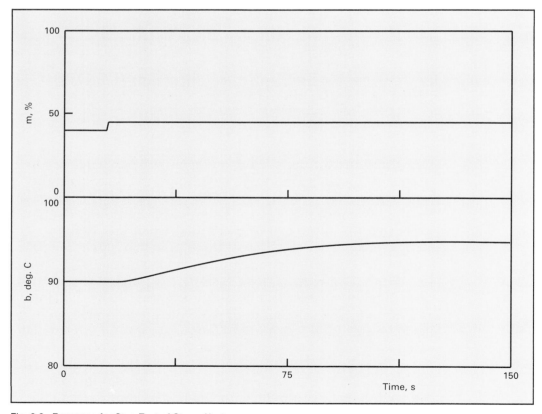

Fig. 3-3. Response for Step Test of Steam Heater.

the time constant, and the dead time. Most controller tuning methods require these three parameters for estimating the controller parameters, as will be shown in the units that follow. For a given process, the gain indicates how much the controlled variable changes for a given change in controller output; the time constant indicates how fast the controlled variable changes; and the dead time indicates how long it takes for the controller to detect the beginning of change in transmitter output. Each of these parameters can be determined from a simple step test.

The steady-state gain or, simply, gain is one of the most important parameters that characterize a process. It is a measure of the sensitivity of the process output to changes in its input. The gain is defined as the steady-state change in output divided by the change in input that caused it:

$$K = \frac{\text{Change in output}}{\text{Change in input}} = \frac{\Delta b_s}{\Delta m} \qquad (3\text{-}1)$$

where:

K = the process gain, % transmitter output/% controller output (%T.O./%C.O.)

Δb_s = the change in transmitter signal, % transmitter output (%T.O.)

Δm = the change in controller output, % controller output (%C.O.)

As can be seen in Fig. 3-3, the change in output, Δb_s, is measured after the process reaches a new steady state. It can thus be assumed that this is a self-regulating process (one that reaches a new steady state when driven by a steady change in input). Two types of processes are not self-regulating: imbalanced or integrating processes and open-loop unstable processes. A typical example of an imbalanced process is the liquid level in a tank, and an example of an unstable process is an exothermic chemical reactor. It is obviously impractical to perform step tests on processes that are not self-regulating. Fortunately, most processes are self-regulating.

From Eq. (3-1) it is evident that the process gain has units of transmitter output divided by controller output. The numerical value of the gain for a given process is the same whether it is expressed in mA/mA (electronic controller), psi/psi (pneumatic controller), or percent transmitter output per percent controller output (%T.O./%C.O.). The latter units are the most commonly used with modern digital controllers and are the ones that will be used in this text. The important point is that the units of the process gain to be used in the controller tuning formulas must be dimensionless.

The gain defined by Eq. (3-1) includes the gains of the transmitter, the process, and the control valve. This is because, as illustrated in Fig. 3-2, these three blocks are essentially combined into one. It is common practice, however, to express the transmitter signal in the engineering units of the measured variable, in which case it is necessary to convert the value of the gain to dimensionless units. This is illustrated in the following example.

Example 3-1, Estimation of the Gain from the Step Response: In the step test of Fig. 3-3, a 0.8-mA change in controller output causes a steady-state change in temperature of 5.0°C. In these units, the value of the gain is:

$$K = (95.0 - 90.0)/0.8 = 6.25°C/mA$$

To convert to dimensionless units, both the change in controller output and the change in temperature must be converted to percent of range, for which the transmitter range is needed. The percent change in controller output is:

$$\Delta m = (0.8 \text{ mA}) (100 - 0)\%C.O./(20 - 4) \text{ mA} = 5.0\% \text{ C.O.}$$

The transmitter range for the steam heater is 50-150°C, thus the change in transmitter output signal is:

$$\Delta b = (5.0°C) (100 - 0)\%T.O./(150 - 50)°C = 5.0\% \text{ T.O.}$$

Thus, the dimensionless process gain is:

$$K = 5.0\% \text{ T.O.}/5.0\% \text{ C.O.} = 1.0\% \text{ T.O.}/\%C.O.$$

By using percent of range for the units of the signals, the solution is equally valid for electronic, pneumatic, and computer control systems.

This example illustrates that it is important to keep track of the units of the gain when tuning controllers. It is evident that a controller cannot be successfully tuned if the value of 6.25 is used for the process gain when the value that must be used is 1.0 or vice versa.

3-3. Estimation of Time Constant and Dead Time

Just as the gain is a measure of the steady-state sensitivity of the controlled process, the time constant and the dead time are measures of its dynamic response. The time constant is a measure of how long it takes the process to reach a new steady state after the initial change in output is detected; the dead time is a measure of how long it takes for the initial change in output to be detected after the occurrence of the input change.

As shall be seen later, the ratio of the process dead time to its time constant is a measure of the controllability of a feedback control loop.

There are several methods for estimating the process time constant and dead time from the step response. The first of these was originally proposed by Ziegler and Nichols in the early 1940s (Reference 5). A slightly different form, called the "tangent" method, is presented here. The other two methods, the "tangent-and-point" method and the "two-point" method, give more reproducible results than the tangent method. The constructions required to estimate the time constant and the dead time are shown in Fig. 3-4, which is basically a reproduction of the step response of Fig. 3-3 showing the constructions needed to analyze it.

The tangent method requires the drawing of the tangent to the response line at the point of maximum rate of change or "inflection point," as shown in Fig. 3-4. The time constant is then defined as the distance in the time axis between the point where the tangent crosses the initial steady state of the output variable, and the point where it crosses the new steady-state value. The dead time is the distance in the time axis between the occurrence of the input step change and the point where the tangent line crosses the initial steady state. These estimates are indicated in Fig. 3-4. The basic problem with the tangent method is that the drawing of the tangent is not very reproducible, creating significant variance in the estimates of the process time constant and dead time. Another problem with the tangent method is that it results in a too long estimate of the process time constant and, thus, in tighter controller tuning than the two methods to be presented next.

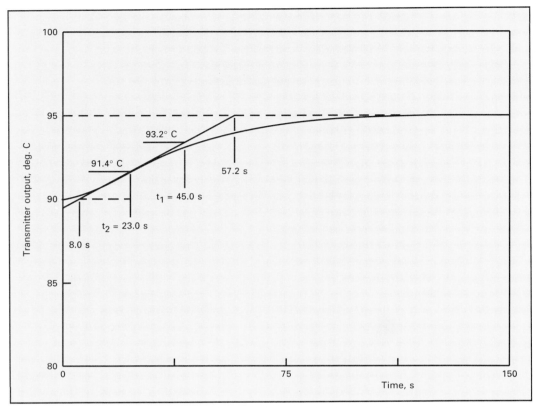

Fig. 3-4. Graphical Determination of Time Constant and Dead Time from Step Response of Steam Heater.

The tangent-and-point method differs from the tangent method in the estimate of the time constant, but it estimates the dead time in exactly the same way. In this method it is necessary to determine the point at which the step response reaches 63.2% of its total steady-state change. This point is marked as t_1 in Fig. 3-4. The time constant is then the period of time between the point where the tangent line crosses the initial steady state and the point where the response reaches 63.2% of the total change. Thus, the time constant is calculated by:

$$\tau = t_1 - t_0 \qquad (3\text{-}2)$$

where τ is the process time constant and t_0 is the dead time. This method results in a shorter estimate of the time constant and, thus, in more conservative controller tuning than the tangent method. However, notice that both estimates of the dead time and the time constant are dependent upon the drawing of the tangent line. This is because the 63.2% point fixes only the sum of the dead time and the time constant, making each individual estimate dependent upon the location of the tangent line, the least reproducible step of the procedure. Because of this, Dr. Cecil Smith (Reference 4) proposed the two-point method, which does not require the drawing of the tangent line.

The two-point method makes use of the 63.2% point defined in the previous method and one other point: the point where the step response reaches 28.3% of its total steady-state change. This point is marked in Fig. 3-4 as t_2. Actually, any two points in the region of maximum rate of change of the response would do, but the two points chosen by Smith result in the following simple estimation formulas for the time constant and the dead time:

$$\tau = 1.5\ (t_1 - t_2) \tag{3-3}$$

$$t_0 = t_1 - \tau \tag{3-4}$$

The reason the two points should be in the region of maximum rate of change is that otherwise small errors in the ordinate would cause large errors in the estimates of t_1 and t_2. The two-point method results in longer estimates of the dead time and shorter estimates of the time constant than the tangent-and-point method, but it is more reproducible because it does not require the drawing of the tangent line. This feature is particularly useful when the response is in the form of sampled values stored in a computer, in which case the values of t_1 and t_2 can be determined by interpolation and it is not even necessary to plot the response. In fact, the computer could be easily programmed to compute the estimates of the time constant and the dead time from the recorded step response data.

The following example illustrates the three methods for determining the dynamic parameters of the process from the step response.

Example 3-2, Gain and Time Constant of Steam Heater: The step response of Fig. 3-4 is for a step change of 5% (0.8 mA) in the output of the temperature controller of the steam heater of Fig. 3-1. This response is an expanded version of the response of Fig. 3-3 that was used in Example 3-1 to determine the process gain; as before, the steady-state change in temperature is 5°C, or 5% of the transmitter range of 50-150°C. The process gain was determined in Example 3-1 as 1.0%/%. In this example the process time constant and the dead time will be determined by each of the methods presented in the preceding discussion.

Tangent Method. The necessary construction of the tangent to the response at the point of maximum rate of change (inflection point) is shown in Fig. 3-4. The values of the dead time and time constant are then determined from the intersection of the tangent line with the initial and final steady-state lines:

Dead time
  (from Fig. 3-4): $t_0 = 8.0$ s (0.13 min)
Time constant: $\tau = 57.2 - 8.0 = 49.2$ s (0.82 min)

Tangent-and-Point Method. The estimate of the dead time is the same as for the tangent method. To determine the time constant, first determine the point t_1 at which the response reaches 63.2% of the total steady-state change:

63.2% point: $T = 90.0 + 0.632(5.0) = 93.2$°C
From Fig. 3-4: $t_1 = 45.0$ s
Time constant: $\tau = 45.0 - 8.0 = 37.0$ s (0.62 min)

Two-Point Method. In addition to the 63.2% point, already determined in the previous method, the 28.3% point is necessary:

28.3% point: $T = 90.0 + 0.283(5.0) = 91.4$°C
From Fig. 3-4: $t_2 = 23.0$ s

Time constant, from Eq. (3-3):

$$\tau = 1.5(45.0 - 23.0) = 33.0 \text{ s } (0.55 \text{ min})$$

Dead time, from Eq. (3-3):

$$t_0 = 45.0 - 33.0 = 12.0 \text{ s } (0.20 \text{ min})$$

As previously indicated, the two-point method results in a higher estimate of the dead time and a lower estimate of the time constant than the other two methods, while the tangent method is at the other extreme. Of the three methods, the two-point method is the easiest to use because it requires only the reading of two points from the response curve.

3-4. Physical Significance of the Time Constant

Armed with the knowledge of how to estimate the process time constant and the dead time from an open-loop step test, it is now wise to examine the physical significance of these two dynamic measures of the process. This will allow estimation of the process time constant and the dead time from physical process characteristics (e.g., volumes, flow rates, valve sizes) when it is not convenient to perform the step test. This section concerns the time constant, and the next section explores the dead time.

To understand the physical significance of the time constant, it is necessary to look at some physical systems whose dynamic response can be characterized by a single time constant and no dead time. Such systems consist of a single capacitance to store mass, energy, momentum, or electricity and a conductance to the flow of these quantities. Such single capacitance/conductance systems are called first-order systems or first-order lags. A number of first-order systems are sketched in Fig. 3-5.

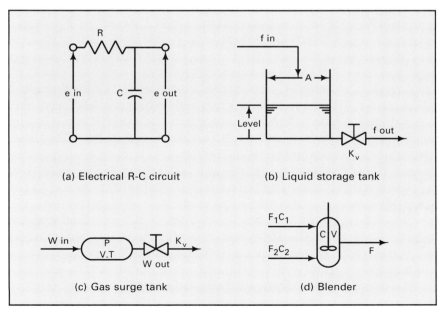

Fig. 3-5. Typical Physical Systems with First-Order Dynamic Response.

The time constant of a first-order system is defined as the ratio of its capacitance to its conductance, or the product of the capacitance times the resistance (the resistance is the reciprocal of the conductance):

$$\tau = \frac{\text{capacitance}}{\text{conductance}} = \text{capacitance} \times \text{resistance} \qquad (3\text{-}5)$$

The concepts of capacitance, resistance, and conductance are best understood by analyzing the physical systems of Fig. 3-5. In each of them is a physical quantity that is conserved, a rate of flow of that quantity, and a potential that drives the flow. The capacitance is defined by the amount of the quantity conserved per unit of potential:

$$\text{capacitance} = \frac{\text{amount of quantity conserved}}{\text{potential}} \qquad (3\text{-}6)$$

The conductance is the ratio of the flow to the potential that drives it:

$$\text{conductance} = \frac{\text{flow of quantity conserved}}{\text{potential}} \qquad (3\text{-}7)$$

A look at the physical systems of Fig. 3-5 will give more specific physical meanings to the terms just presented.

Electrical System [Fig. 3-5(a)]

For this system the quantity conserved is electric charge, the potential is electric voltage, and the flow is electric current. The capacitance is provided by the ability of the capacitor to store electric charge, and the conductance is the reciprocal of the resistance of the electrical resistor. The time constant is then given by:

$$\tau = RC \qquad (3\text{-}8)$$

where R is the resistance of the electrical resistor in ohms, and C is the capacitance of the electrical capacitor in farads. The time constant is in seconds.

Liquid Storage Tank [Fig. 3-5(b)]

In this common process system the quantity conserved is the volume of liquid (assuming constant density), the capacitance is provided by the ability of the tank to store liquid, and the potential for flow through the valve is provided by the level of liquid in the tank. The capacitance is the volume of liquid per unit level (the cross-sectional area of the tank), and the conductance is the change in flow through the valve per unit change in level. The time constant can then be estimated by:

$$\tau = A/K_v \qquad (3\text{-}9)$$

where A is the cross-sectional area of the tank, ft^2, and K_v is the conductance of the valve, (ft^3/min)/ft. The conductance of the valve depends on the valve size and percent of lift, usually known in terms of flow per unit pressure drop. Notice that the change in pressure drop across the valve per unit change in level can be calculated by multiplying the density of the liquid times the local acceleration of gravity.

Gas Surge Tank [Fig. 3-5(c)]

This system is analogous to the liquid storage tank. The quantity conserved is the mass of gas, the potential that drives the flow through the valve is the pressure in the tank, and the capacitance is provided by the ability of the tank to store gas as it is compressed. The capacitance can be calculated by the formula MV/zRT lb/psi, where V is the volume of the tank, R is the ideal gas constant (10.73 psi-ft^3/lbmol-R), z is the compressibility of the gas, M is its molecular weight, and T is its absolute temperature. The conductance of the valve is expressed in change of mass flow per unit change in pressure drop across the valve. The time constant of the tank can be estimated by the formula:

$$\tau = (MV/zRT)/K_v \qquad (3\text{-}10)$$

where K_v is the conductance of the valve, (lb/min)/psi.

Blending Tank [Fig. 3-5(d)]

Change of temperature and change of composition in a blending tank are governed by the phenomena of convection transfer of energy and mass, respectively. Assuming that the tank is perfectly mixed, the capacitance is provided by the ability of the material in the tank (usually a liquid) to store energy and mass of the various components of the mixture entering the tank, and the conductance is the total flow through the tank. The potential for energy transfer is the temperature and, for mass transfer, the concentration of each component. In the absence of chemical reactions and heat transfer through the walls of the blender, the time constant for both temperature and composition is given by:

$$\tau = V/F \tag{3-11}$$

where V is the volume of the tank, ft^3, and F is the total flow through the tank, ft^3/min.

If there is a chemical reaction, the time constant for the concentration of reactants is decreased because the conductance is increased to the sum (F + kV), where k is the reaction coefficient, defined here as the change in reaction rate divided by the change in the reactant concentration. The conductances are added because the processes of reaction and convection occur in parallel.

Similarly, if there is heat transfer to the surroundings or to a coil or jacket, the time constant for temperature changes is reduced because the conductance is increased to the sum [F + (UA/ρC_p)], where U is the coefficient of heat transfer (Btu/min-ft^2-°F), A is the heat transfer area (ft^2), ρ is the density of the fluid (lb/ft^3), and C_p is the heat capacity of the fluid (Btu/lb-°F). In this case the conductances are additive because the processes of conduction and convection occur in parallel.

For the preceding examples of first-order processes it is possible to estimate the process time constant from process parameters, and, thus, it is not necessary to perform a dynamic test on the process. For more complex processes such as distillation columns and heat exchangers, which represent higher-order systems, the time constant cannot be estimated. Such systems are made up of many resistance-capacitance combinations in series and in parallel. For these systems there is no other recourse than some form of dynamic testing such as the one described at the beginning of this unit.

Example 3-3, Estimation of the Time Constant of a Surge Tank: The surge tank of Fig. 3-5(c) is for an air compressor. It runs at a temperature of 150°F, and has a volume of 10 ft^3. The valve can pass a flow of 100 lb/hr at a pressure drop of 5 psi when the pressure in the tank is 30 psig. Estimate the time constant of the tank for variations in pressure.

The capacitance of the tank is its ability to store air as its density changes with pressure, which is the potential for flow. Assuming that air at 30 psig behaves as an ideal gas (z = 1), and using the fact that its molecular weight, M, is 29, the capacitance is:

$$capacitance = VM/RT$$

$$= (10) (29)/(10.73) (150 + 460)$$

$$= 0.0443 \text{ lb/psi}$$

The conductance of the valve can be estimated from the formulas given by valve manufacturers to size the valves. Because the pressure drop through the valve is small compared to the pressure in the tank, the flow is "subcritical," and the conductance can be determined by the following formula:

$$K = W (1 + \Delta P_v/P_1)/(2\Delta P_v)$$

$$= (100/60) [1 + 5/(30 + 14.7)]/[(2) (5)]$$

$$= 0.1853 \text{ (lb/min)/psi}$$

The time constant is then:

$$\tau = 0.0443/0.1853$$

$$= 0.24 \text{ min } (14.3 \text{ s})$$

The conductance calculated for the valve is the change in gas flow per unit change in tank pressure, P_1. It considers the variation in gas density with pressure, and the variation in flow with the square root of the product of density times the pressure drop across the valve, ΔP_v. For critical flow, when the pressure drop across the valve is more than one half the upstream pressure, the conductance can be calculated by the formula: $K_v = W/P_1$.

3-5. Physical Significance of Dead Time

Pure dead time (transportation lag or time delay) occurs when the process variable is transported from one point to another, hence the term "transportation lag". At any point in time, the variable downstream is what the variable upstream was one dead time before, hence the term "time delay". When the

variable first starts changing at the upstream point, it takes
one dead time before the downstream variable starts changing,
hence the term "dead time". This is all illustrated in Fig. 3-6.
The dead time can be estimated from the following formula:

$$t_0 = \text{distance/velocity} \qquad (3\text{-}12)$$

Different physical variables travel at different velocities, as
follows:

- Electric voltage and current travel at the velocity of light,
  300,000 km/s (984,000,000 ft/s).
- Pressure and flow travel at the velocity of sound in the
  fluid, e.g., 340 m/s (1,100 ft/s) for air at ambient
  temperature.
- Temperature, composition, and other fluid properties travel
  at the velocity of the fluid. up to about 5 m/s (15 ft/s) for
  liquids, and up to about 60 m/s (200 ft/s) for gases.
- Solid properties vary at the velocity of the solid, e.g., paper
  in a paper machine, coal in a conveyor.

From these numbers we can see that, for the reasonable
distances that are typical of process control systems, pure
dead time is significant only for temperature, composition,
and other fluid and solid properties. The velocity of the fluid
in a pipe can be calculated by the following formula:

$$v = F/A_p \qquad (3\text{-}13)$$

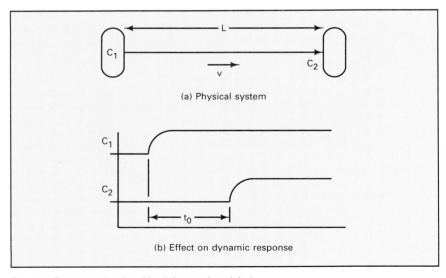

(a) Physical system

(b) Effect on dynamic response

Fig. 3-6. Transportation Lag (dead time or time delay).

where:

> v   is the average velocity, ft/s
> F   is the volumetric flow, ft^3/s
> A_p is the cross-sectional area of the pipe, ft^2

Given that (as will be seen shortly) the dead time makes a feedback loop less controllable, most process control loops are designed to reduce the dead time as much as possible. Dead time can be reduced by installing the sensor as close to the equipment as possible, using electronic instead of pneumatic instrumentation, etc.

Although pure dead time is usually not significant for most processes, the process dead time that is estimated from the step test arises not necessarily from transportation lag, but from the presence of two or more first-order processes in series (e.g., the trays in a distillation column). When these processes are modeled with a first-order model, dead time is needed to represent the delay caused by the lags in series. As an example, Fig. 3-7 shows the response of composition in a blending train when it consists of one, two, five, and ten tanks in series, assuming that the total blending volume is the same; e.g., each of the ten tanks has one tenth the volume of the single tank. In the limit, an infinite number of infinitesimal tanks in series results in a pure dead time equal to the time constant of the single tank.

Most real processes fall somewhere between the two extremes of first-order (perfectly mixed) processes and transportation (unmixed) processes. The first-order plus dead time (FOPDT) model used earlier for such processes is the simplest model for characterizing them.

Example 3-4, Estimation of Dead Time: Estimate the dead time of temperature of a liquid flowing through a 1-inch standard pipe at 10 gpm. The distance the fluid must travel is 100 ft.

A pipe manual or engineering handbook will show that the cross-sectional area of the pipe is A_p = 0.00600 ft^2. The velocity of the fluid in the pipe is then:

$$v = (10 \text{ gpm})/[(7.48 \text{ gal/ft}^3) \ (60 \text{ s/min}) \ (0.00600 \text{ ft}^2)]$$

$$= 3.71 \text{ ft/s}$$

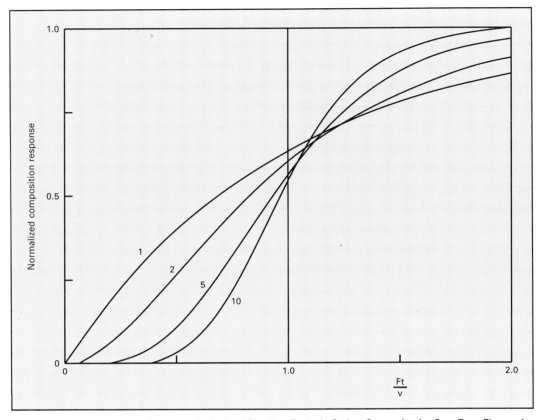

Fig. 3-7. Response of Composition out of a Train of Blending Tanks in Series. Curves Are for One, Two, Five, and Ten Tanks in Series, Keeping in Each Case the Total Volume of All the Tanks the Same.

Dead time:

$$t_0 = (100 \text{ ft})/(3.71 \text{ ft/s})$$

$$= 26.9 \text{ s} \quad (0.45 \text{ min})$$

3-6. Effect of Process Nonlinearities

A common characteristic of most chemical processes is that they are nonlinear. There are, in general, two types of nonlinearities: those that arise from the variation of dynamic parameters with operating conditions, and those that result from saturation of the final control elements (e.g., control valves driven against their upper or lower operating limits).

Because most process control strategies are linear, the variation of the process gain, time constant, and dead time with process operating conditions causes the controller performance to vary as process conditions change. The best that can be done is to tune the controller so that its performance is best at the design operating point and acceptable over the expected range of operating conditions.

It is easily deduced that, for concentration and temperature, the time constant and the dead time vary with process throughput: Equations (3-11), (3-12), and (3-13) show that the time constant and the dead time are inversely proportional to the flow and, thus, to the throughput. From Eqs. (3-9) and (3-10) it can be seen that, for liquid level and gas pressure, the time constant varies with the valve conductance, K_v, which, being a function of the valve characteristics and of the pressure drop across the valve, usually varies. Control valve characteristics are usually selected to maintain the process gain constant, which, for liquid level and gas pressure, is equivalent to keeping the valve conductance constant (the gain for these variables is the reciprocal of the valve conductance).

Of the three parameters of a process, the gain has the greatest influence on the performance of the control system. As pointed out in the preceding paragraph, such devices as equal percentage control valve characteristics are used to maintain the process gain as constant as possible. The equal percentage characteristics, shown in Fig. 3-8, are particularly useful in maintaining a constant gain because the gain of most rate processes (e.g., fluid flow, heat transfer, mass transfer) decreases as the flow increases, that is, as the valve opens. As Fig. 3-8 shows, the gain or sensitivity of an equal percentage valve increases as the valve is opened, compensating for the decrease in the process gain.

The other type of process nonlinearity is caused by saturation of the controller output and of the final control element, not necessarily at the same points. Saturation gives rise to various degrees of the problem known as reset windup, in which the reset or integral mode drives the controller output against one of its limits. Reset windup is worse when the controller output limit is different from the corresponding limit of its destination (e.g., the position of the control valve). For example, in a pneumatic control installation, control valves operate in the range of 3 to 15 psig air pressure; but the controllers, if not properly protected against windup, can operate between 0 and 20 psig.

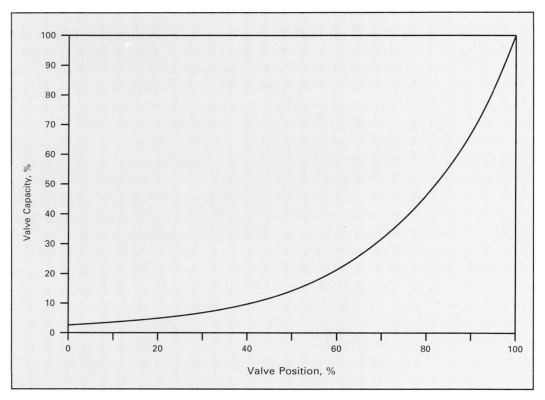

Fig. 3-8. Equal Percentage Characteristics of a Control Valve.

Reset windup is more common in batch processes and during start-up and shutdown of continuous processes, but the possibility of windup must always be kept in mind when tuning controllers. Some apparent tuning problems are really caused by unexpected reset windup. (Reset windup will be examined in more detail in section 5-7.)

The following example illustrates the variation of the process gain in a steam heater. It takes advantage of the fact that the gain can be calculated from a simple steady-state energy balance on the heater.

Example 3-5, Variation in Steam Heater Gain with Process Flow: At design conditions, the process flow through the heater of Fig. 3-1 is F = 12 kg/s, its inlet temperature is T_i = 50 °C, and it is desired to heat it to T = 90 °C. The process fluid has a specific heat of C_p = 3.75 kJ/kg-°C, and the steam supplies H_v = 2250 kJ/kg upon condensing. Heat losses to the surroundings can be neglected. The temperature transmitter range is 50 to 150°C; and the control valve is linear, with constant pressure drop, and delivers 2.0 kg/s of steam when fully opened. Calculate the gain of the heater in terms of the sensitivity of the outlet temperature to changes in steam flow.

In Example 3-1 it was determined from a step test that the gain of the heater is 1.0%/% at the design conditions. This example will verify this value from a steady-state energy balance on the heater and examine its dependence on process flow.

An energy balance on the heater, neglecting heat losses, gives the following formula:

$$FC_p(T - T_i) = F_sH_v$$

where F_s is the steam flow and the other terms have been defined in the statement of the problem. The gain is the steady-state change in outlet temperature per unit change in steam flow:

$$K = \frac{\Delta T}{\Delta F_s} = \frac{H_v}{FC_p}$$

Notice that the gain is inversely proportional to the process flow F. From this formula, the units of the gain are °C/(kg/s). To convert it to %T.O./%C.O. (dimensionless), multiply by the range of the valve (2.0 kg/s) and divide by the span of the transmitter (100°C). This results in the following:

F, kg/s	K, °C/(kg/s)	K, %T.O./%C.O.
3.0	200.0	4.0
6.0	100.0	2.0
12.0	50.0	1.0
18.0	33.3	0.67

This example shows the variation of the process gain, indicating that the steam heater is nonlinear. As mentioned earlier, the decrease in process gain with an increase in flow is characteristic of many process control systems, hence the popularity of equal percentage control valves, which exactly compensate for this gain variation.

3-7. Testing Batch Processes

Dynamic testing of batch processes differs from continuous process testing in that the base conditions around which the process is disturbed are not constant with time. In other words, in the step testing procedure presented earlier in this unit, the reference for the test was assumed to be constant, but this is not always the case when testing batch processes. This section shows that the step test can still be performed on a batch process, as long as the parameters are measured by taking the difference between the response to the test and the base response.

The base response is the controlled variable profile for the batch when the manipulated variable is maintained at the base or design conditions. Then, when the manipulated variable is changed, a different profile is obtained for the controlled variable. The response from which the process parameters must be estimated is the difference between the two profiles. This procedure will be demonstrated in the following example.

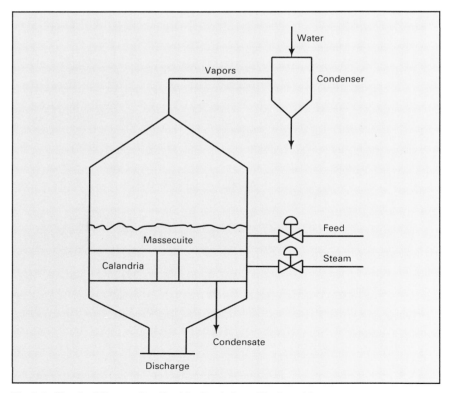

Fig. 3-9. Sketch of Vacuum Pan Used for Batch Crystallization of Sugar.

Example 3-6, Step Testing of a Vacuum Pan: In the production of cane sugar, a key step is the separation of the sugar from impurities by batch crystallization in a vacuum pan. A sketch of the vacuum pan is shown in Fig. 3-9. To produce sugar crystals of uniform size in a reasonable time, it is important to control the supersaturation of sugar in the massecuite (mother liquor) and its mobility (viscosity). The manipulated variables are the syrup feed rate and the steam rate. The syrup is fed continuously during the batch to replenish the sugar in the massecuite, and the steam condenses in a calandria (donut-shaped basket of heat exchange tubes) to evaporate the water fed with the syrup.

The base profile of the supersaturation is shown in Fig. 3-10.

The supersaturation profile after application of a step change in steam rate is also shown in the figure. The step response is then given by the difference between the two curves. These curves were obtained from a computer simulation of the pan reported by Qi Liwu and Corripio (Reference 2). They would

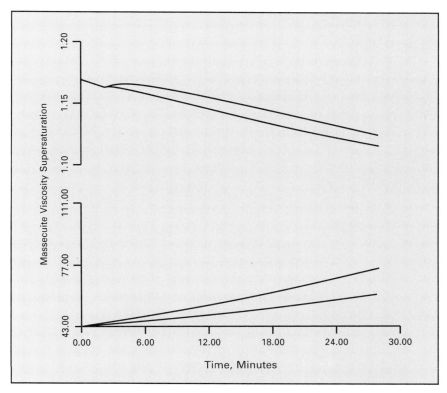

Fig. 3-10. Base Profile and Profile after a Step Change in the Steam Flow to the Vacuum Pan. The Step Response Is the Difference between the Two Profiles.

be difficult to obtain from an actual pan because they involve running two batches with the steam valve held constant. The curves are presented here to illustrate the procedure for the dynamic testing of batch processes.

3-8. Summary

This unit showed how to perform and analyze a process step test to determine the parameters of a first-order plus dead time (FOPDT) model of the process: the gain, the time constant, and the dead time. The physical significance of these parameters and how to estimate them for some simple process loops was presented. In the units to follow, these parameters will be used to design and tune feedback, feedforward, and multivariable controllers.

Regardless of the method used to measure the dynamic characteristics of a process, it is important to realize that even a rough estimate of the process dynamic parameters can be quite helpful in one's efforts to tune and troubleshoot process control systems.

Exercises

3-1. Summarize the procedure for performing a step test on a process.

3-2. Which are the parameters of a first-order plus dead time (FOPDT) model of the process? Give a brief description of each one.

3-3. A change of 100 lb/hr in the set point of a steam flow controller to the reboiler of a distillation column results in a change in the bottoms temperature of 2°F. The steam flow transmiter has a range of 0 to 5000 lb/hr, and the temperature transmitter has a calibrated range of 200°F to 250°F. Calculate the process gain for the temperature loop in °F/(lb/hr) and in %T.O./%C.O.

3-4. In tuning feedforward control systems the FOPDT parameters of the process are needed for step changes in the disturbance and in the manipulated variable. The figure below shows the response of the steam heater outlet temperature of Fig. 3-1 to a step change of 2 kg/s in process flow. Determine the gain, time constant, and dead time for this response using the slope method, and the slope-and-point method.

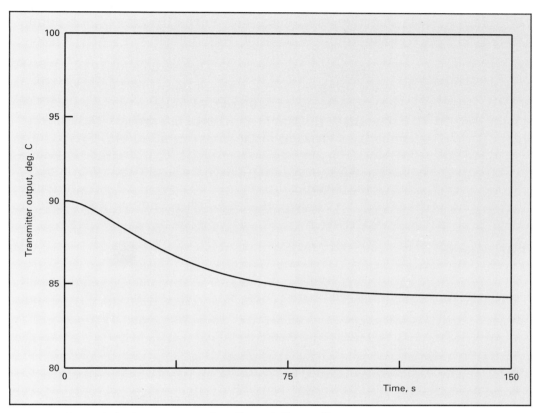

Response of Heater Outlet Temperature to a Step Change in Process Flow.

3-5. Repeat 3-4 using the two-point method.

3-6. A passive low-pass filter can be built with a resistor and a capacitor. For use in printed circuit boards, maximum sizes of these components are, respectively, 10 megohms (million ohms) and 100 microfarads (millionth of a farad). What would then be the maximum time constant of a filter built with these components?

3-7. The surge tank of Fig. 3-5(b) has an area of 50 ft^2 and the valve has a conductance of 50 gpm/ft of level change (1 ft^3 = 7.48 gallons). Estimate the time constant of the response of the level.

3-8. The blender of Fig. 3-5(d) has a volume of 2000 gallons. Calculate the time constant of the composition response for product flows of (a) 50 gpm, (b) 500 gpm, and (c) 5000 gpm.

3-9. The blender of Fig. 3-5(d) mixes 100 gpm of concentrated solution at 20 lb/gallon with 400 gpm of dilute solution at 2 lb/gallon. Calculate the steady-state product concentration in lb/gallon. How much would the outlet concentration change if the concentrated solution rate were to change to 110 gpm, all other conditions remaining the same? Calculate the process gain for the change suggested in the previous question.

3-10. Repeat 3-9 assuming the initial rates are 10 gpm of concentrated solution and 40 gpm of dilute solution, and the concentrated solution is changed to 11 gpm to do the test.

References

1. Luyben, W. L., *Process Modeling, Simulation, and Control for Chemical Engineers*, 2nd ed. (New York: McGraw-Hill, 1990).
2. Qi Liwu and Corripio, A. B., "Dynamic Matrix Control of Sugar Cristalization in a Vacuum Pan," *Proceedings of ISA/85* (Research Triangle Park, NC: ISA, 1985).
3. Smith, C. A., and Corripio, A. B., *Principles and Practice of Automatic Process Control* (New York: Wiley, 1985).
4. Smith, C. L., *Digital Computer Process Control* (Scranton, PA: International Textbook Co., 1972).
5. Ziegler, J. G., and Nichols, N. B., "Optimum Settings for Automatic Controllers," *Transactions ASME*, V. 64 (Nov. 1942), p. 759.

Unit 4:
How To Tune Feedback Controllers

UNIT 4

How To Tune Feedback Controllers

Unit 2 established how to tune controllers by the on-line or ultimate gain method and that the ultimate gain has two major limitations: it gives only one criterion of performance (the quarter-decay ratio response), and it requires a very empirical characterization of the process (the ultimate gain and period). This unit offers several alternative methods for tuning controllers, all based on a more fundamental characterization of process response: the gain, time constant, and dead time model of Unit 3. In this unit also are different sets of formulas for tuning the controller for performance criteria other than quarter-decay ratio.

Learning Objectives — When you have completed this unit you should:

A. Know how to tune feedback controllers for several closed-loop performance criteria from the gain, the time constant, and the dead time parameters of the process.

B. Understand the definition of the various minimum error integral criteria for the closed-loop response.

C. Differentiate between tuning for disturbance and set point changes.

4-1. Tuning for Quarter-Decay Ratio Response

Besides the formulas for quarter-decay ratio (QDR) response tuning based on the ultimate gain and period of the loop (see Table 2-1 in Unit 2), Ziegler and Nichols (Reference 4) also developed formulas for tuning feedback controllers for QDR response that are based on process gain, K, time constant, τ, and dead time, t_0. These formulas are given in Table 4-1.

These formulas are very similar to those of Table 2-1. Notice, for example, that in both sets of formulas the proportional gain of the PI controller is 10% lower and the PID gain is 20% higher than that of the P controller, and that the derivative or rate time is one fourth the integral or reset time. The ratio of the integral time of the PI controller to that of the PID controller is also the same for both sets of formulas, or about 1.7 times faster reset action when derivative is used than when it is not.

TABLE 4-1. TUNING FORMULAS FOR QUARTER-DECAY RATIO RESPONSE

	Gain	Integral Time	Derivative Time
P	$K_c = \tau/Kt_0$	—	—
PI	$K_c = 0.9\tau/Kt_0$	$T_I = 3.33t_0$	—
PID Series	$K'_c = 1.2\tau/Kt_0$	$T'_I = 2.0\ t_0$	$T'_D = 0.5t_0$

The formulas of Table 4-1, however, give important insight on how the parameters of the process affect the tuning of the controller and, thus, the performance of the loop. Three major conclusions can be drawn from the formulas:

1. The controller gain is shown to be inversely proportional to the "process" gain K. Since the process gain represents the product of all the elements in the loop other than the controller (control valve, process equipment, and sensor/transmitter), this means that the loop response depends on the "loop gain," that is, the product of all of the elements in the loop. It also means that if the gain of any of the elements were to change because of recalibration, resizing, or nonlinearity (see section 3-6), the response of the feedback loop will change unless the controller gain is readjusted.

2. The controller gain must be reduced when the ratio of the process dead time to its time constant increases. This means that the controllability of the loop decreases when the ratio of the process dead time to its time constant increases, and leads to the definition of the ratio of dead time to time constant as the "uncontrollability parameter" of the loop:

$$P_u = \frac{t_0}{\tau} \tag{4-1}$$

where t_0 is the process dead time and τ is its time constant.

Notice that having a long dead time parameter means that the loop is less controllable only if the time constant is short. In other words, a loop with a dead time of several minutes would be just as controllable as one with a dead time of a few seconds if the ratio of dead time to time constant for both loops is the same.

3. The speed of response of the controller, which is determined by the integral and derivative times, must match the speed of response of the process. The QDR formulas match these response speeds by relating the

controller time parameters to the process dead time. Later
there will be formulas that relate them to the process time
constant and the uncontrollability parameter.

These three conclusions can be very helpful in guiding the
tuning of feedback controllers, even in such cases when the
tuning formulas cannot be used directly because the process
parameters cannot be determined. For example, if the
performance of a well-tuned controller were to deteriorate
under operation, one would look for either a change in the
process gain, its uncontrollability parameter, or its speed of
response. Many times difficulties in tuning the controller may
arise because of trying to bring the controlled variable back to
its set point faster than the process can respond (with too
short an integral time).

Coupled with the methods for estimating time constants and
dead times given in sections 3-4 and 3-5, the conclusions
drawn from the tuning formulas can also help in designing the
process and its instrumentation. For example, the
controllability of the loop can be improved by reducing the
dead time between the manipulated variable and the sensor or
by increasing the process time constant. Also the effect of
process, control valve, and sensor nonlinearities on the
variability of the loop gain can be quantitatively estimated,
thus determining the need for readjusting the controller gain
when process conditions change.

Applying the QDR Tuning Formulas

The formulas of Table 4-1 were developed empirically for the
most common range of the process uncontrollability
parameter, which is between 0.1 and 0.3, based on the fact
that most processes do not exhibit significant transportation
lag (rather, the dead time is the result of several time
constants in series).

For the PID controller, the formulas apply to the series
formula (see Eq. (2-10) and Fig. 2-11), given that the parallel
formula was not implemented on digital computers until over
two decades after Ziegler and Nichols developed the QDR
tuning methods.

The QDR formulas were developed for continuous analog
controllers and, thus, must be adjusted for the sampling

frequency of digital controllers (computer control algorithms, distributed controllers or microprocessor-based controllers). Moore, et al., (Reference 2) propose that the process dead time be increased by one half the sampling period to account for the fact that the controller output is held constant for one sampling period, where the sampling period is the time between updates of the controller output. Following this procedure, the uncontrollability parameter for digital controllers is:

$$P_u = \frac{t_0 + T/2}{\tau} \qquad (4\text{-}2)$$

where T is the sampling period. Notice that increasing the sampling period reduces the controllability of the loop; that is, the slower the control algorithm processing frequency, the worse the performance of the loop. This does not necessarily mean every loop should be processed as frequently as possible, because there is a point of diminishing returns—a sampling frequency above which the computer load is increased without any significant improvement in control performance. For most loops, control performance does not improve much when the sample time is reduced beyond one tenth the time constant.

4-2. Tuning for Minimum Error Integrals

The tuning formulas for quarter-decay ratio response give acceptable response for most control loops. Their major limitation is the narrow range of the uncontrollability parameter for which they apply. Another difficulty is that, for PI and PID controllers, the QDR response will result from an infinite number of combinations of the controller tuning parameters; that is, for each setting of the integral time on a PI controller and for each reset-derivative time combination on a PID controller, there is a setting of the gain that results in QDR response.

Lopez, et al., (Reference 1) propose a set of tuning formulas for minimizing the absolute integral of the error for disturbance inputs (for bringing the controlled variable back to its set point after a disturbance causes it to deviate from it).

There are several ways of calculating the absolute integral of the error, namely:

Integral of the Absolute Value of the Error (IAE):

$$IAE = \int |e| \, dt \qquad (4\text{-}3)$$

Integral of the Squared Error (ISE):

$$ISE = \int e^2 \, dt \qquad (4\text{-}4)$$

Integral of the Time-Weighted Absolute Value of the Error (ITAE):

$$ITAE = \int t|e| \, dt \qquad (4\text{-}5)$$

Integral of the Time-Weighted Square of the Error (ITSE):

$$ITSE = \int te^2 \, dt \qquad (4\text{-}6)$$

where e is the error or difference between the set point and the measurement, and t is the time from the beginning of the response.

Figure 4-1 graphically illustrates the meaning of these integrals. The tuning formulas for "minimum error integral" response were obtained by correlating the results of computer programs that calculated the combination of controller parameters that minimize these integrals for many sets of values of the process parameters. Each of the integrals emphasizes a different aspect of the closed-loop response: ISE and ITSE weigh large errors more than IAE and ITAE and, thus, result in tighter, more oscillatory responses; ITAE and ITSE put more weight on errors that occur toward the end of the response than on those occurring near the beginning, resulting in larger initial deviations than IAE and ISE. Tables 4-2, 4-3, and 4-4 summarize the formulas obtained by Lopez,

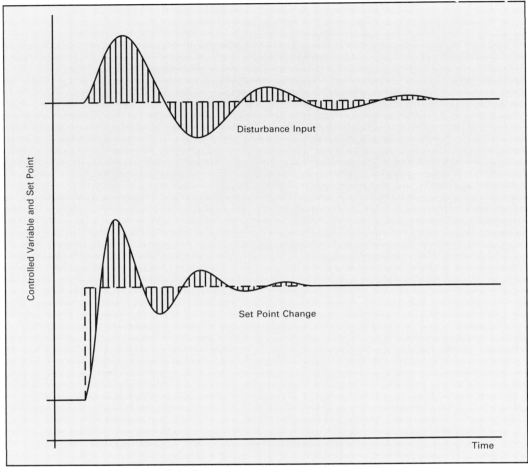

Fig. 4-1. Definition of Error Integral Criteria.

et al., (Reference 1) in terms of process gain, K, time constant, τ, and uncontrollability parameter, P_u [see Eq. (4-2)].

Formulas were not developed for minimum ITSE response. Of the three sets of tuning formulas for minimum integral

TABLE 4-2. TUNING FORMULAS FOR MINIMUM IAE ON DISTURBANCE INPUTS

	Gain	Integral Time	Derivative Time
P	$K_c = \dfrac{0.902}{K} P_u^{-0.985}$	—	—
PI	$K_c = \dfrac{0.984}{K} P_u^{-0.985}$	$T_I = \dfrac{\tau}{0.608} P_u^{0.707}$	—
PID Parallel	$K_c = \dfrac{1.435}{K} P_u^{-0.921}$	$T_I = \dfrac{\tau}{0.878} P_u^{0.749}$	$T_D = 0.482\tau P_u^{1.137}$

TABLE 4-3. TUNING FORMULAS FOR MINIMUM ITAE ON DISTURBANCE INPUTS

	Gain	Integral Time	Derivative Time
P	$K_c = \dfrac{0.490}{K} P_u^{-1.084}$	—	—
PI	$K_c = \dfrac{0.859}{K} P_u^{-0.977}$	$T_I = \dfrac{\tau}{0.674} P_u^{0.680}$	—
PID Parallel	$K_c = \dfrac{1.357}{K} P_u^{-0.947}$	$T_I = \dfrac{\tau}{0.842} P_u^{0.738}$	$T_D = 0.381\tau P_u^{0.995}$

TABLE 4-4. TUNING FORMULAS FOR MINIMUM ISE ON DISTURBANCE INPUTS

	Gain	Integral Time	Derivative Time
P	$K_c = \dfrac{1.411}{K} P_u^{-0.917}$	—	—
PI	$K_c = \dfrac{1.305}{K} P_u^{-0.959}$	$T_I = \dfrac{\tau}{0.492} P_u^{0.739}$	—
PID Parallel	$K_c = \dfrac{1.495}{K} P_u^{-0.945}$	$T_I = \dfrac{\tau}{1.101} P_u^{0.771}$	$T_D = 0.560\tau P_u^{1.006}$

criteria, the ISE formulas result in the tightest tuning (highest gain, shortest integral time), ITAE results in the loosest, and IAE results in intermediate tuning. ITSE formulas would probably fall between IAE and ISE in tightness of tuning.

The same three conclusions can be drawn from the minimum error integral tuning formulas that were drawn from the QDR response formulas: the controller gain is inversely proportional to the process gain, making the response dependent on the loop gain; the optimum loop gain decreases with the ratio of the process dead time to its time constant (that is, with its uncontrollability parameter) [see Eq. (4-2)]; and the speed of response of the controller must match the speed of response of the process.

Unlike the QDR formulas, the minimum error integral formulas relate the integral and derivative times to the time constant of the process rather than to its dead time. The effect of the dead time appears through the uncontrollability parameter, calling for slower reset action and more derivative time with increasing uncontrollability.

Tuning for Set Point Changes

The set of tuning parameters that minimizes the error integral for disturbance inputs is not the same as the set that minimizes it for changes in set point. This is because, when the set point is suddenly changed, the error changes from zero to a finite value instantaneously, while for disturbance inputs the error usually grows gradually, allowing for higher controller gains. The tuning formulas for disturbance inputs presented in Tables 4-2, 4-3, and 4-4 assume that the rate of response for a disturbance input is the same as for a change in the controller output, and that the disturbance change is a sudden and sustained change (a "step change").

Rovira (Reference 3) developed sets of tuning formulas to minimize the error integrals for set point changes. These formulas are given in Tables 4-5 and 4-6, in terms of process gain, K, time constant, τ, and uncontrollability parameter, P_u [see Eq. (4-2)].

These formulas usually give smaller gains and derivative times and longer integral times than the formulas for disturbance inputs. The conclusions drawn from the QDR and disturbance formulas can also be drawn from the formulas of Tables 4-5 and 4-6. Rovira and his co-workers did not develop formulas for proportional controllers because they considered that the minimum error integral criteria was not appropriate for such controllers. They did not develop minimum ISE formulas because they considered them to give very oscillatory responses.

TABLE 4-5. MINIMUM IAE TUNING FORMULAS FOR SET POINT CHANGES

	Gain	**Integral Time**	**Derivative Time**
PI	$K_c = \dfrac{0.758}{K} P_u^{-0.861}$	$T_I = \dfrac{\tau}{1.02 - 0.323P_u}$	—
PID Parallel	$K_c = \dfrac{1.086}{K} P_u^{-0.869}$	$T_I = \dfrac{\tau}{0.74 - 0.130P_u}$	$T_D = 0.348\tau P_u^{0.914}$

TABLE 4-6. MINIMUM ITAE TUNING FORMULAS FOR SET POINT CHANGES

	Gain	**Integral Time**	**Derivative Time**
PI	$K_c = \dfrac{0.586}{K} P_u^{-0.916}$	$T_I = \dfrac{\tau}{1.03 - 0.165P_u}$	—
PID Parallel	$K_c = \dfrac{0.965}{K} P_u^{-0.855}$	$T_I = \dfrac{\tau}{0.80 - 0.147P_u}$	$T_D = 0.308\tau P_u^{0.929}$

Application of Minimum Error Integral Formulas

The formulas given in Tables 4-2 through 4-6 were developed for the continuous analog (electronic and pneumatic) controllers and, thus, when applied to digital controllers (just as the QDR response formulas) must have the dead time adjusted for sampling by adding one half the sampling period to the process dead time [see Eq. (4-2)]. The formulas should not be applied to processes with uncontrollability parameters (ratio of dead time to time constant) outside the range of 0.1 to 1.0, which is the range used to develop the correlations. Finally, the PID formulas apply to the parallel controller—the one described by Eq. (2-9) and sketched in Fig. 2-10(a).

Many digital controllers offer the option of having either the derivative or the proportional mode or both act on the controlled variable instead of on the error. When both of these options are taken, the formulas for disturbance inputs should be used to tune the controller, because then it is possible to use the tighter tuning parameters without danger of excessive overshoot. The formulas for set point changes are most applicable to the slave controllers in cascade control systems, in which case the proportional mode should act on the error signal so that the controller output can respond quickly to the set point changes generated by the master controller (see Unit 7).

4-3. Comparative Examples of Controller Tuning

This section will compare the results of using the various sets of formulas presented in the preceding sections to tune the temperature controller of the steam heater of Fig. 3-1. Recall that the first-order plus dead time model parameters for this exchanger are, from Example 3-2:

$$\text{Gain} = 1.0 \ \%\text{T.O.}/\%\text{C.O.}$$

	Tangent Method	Tangent and Point Method	Two-Point Method
Time constant, min	0.82	0.62	0.55
Dead time, min	0.13	0.13	0.20
Uncontrollability parameter	0.16	0.21	0.36

It is evident that the tuning parameters will depend on which of the three methods is used for determining the time constant

and dead time. Ziegler and Nichols used the tangent method
to develop their empirical formulas, working with actual
processes and physical simulations; thus, the tangent method
should be used when tuning for quarter-decay ratio (QDR)
response. Lopez and Rovira developed their minimum error
integral formulas using true first-order plus dead time models;
thus, any of the three methods can be used to determine the
dead time and time constant to use with their formulas. Notice
that the tangent method will result in the tightest tuning
parameters, while the two-point method will result in the
most conservative tuning parameters.

Example 4-1, Quarter-Decay Ratio (QDR) Tuning: Compare
the performance of the proportional (P), proportional-integral
(PI) and proportional-integral-derivative (PID) controllers
tuned for QDR response on the temperature control of the
steam heater. Use the process parameters estimated by the
tangent method.

The controller tuning parameters, obtained by the formulas of
Table 4-1 with a process gain of 1%/%, time constant of 0.82
min, and dead time of 0.13 min, are:

	K_c, %/%	T_I, min	T_D, min
P	6.2	—	—
PI	5.5	0.44	—
PID series	7.4	0.27	0.07

The response of the heater outlet temperature and the
controller output using these tuning parameters are compared
in Fig. 4-2 for a 10°C step increase in process inlet
temperature. The P and PI controllers produce about the same
maximum initial deviation, while the initial deviation for the
series PID controller is smaller. The P controller is shown to
produce an offset or steady-state error. The advantage of the
derivative mode is obvious: it produces a smaller initial
deviation and maintains the temperature closer to the set point
for the entire response. The PID controller response produced
about one third as much IAE as the PI controller for this
example.

**Example 4-2, Minimum Error Integral PI Tuning for
Disturbance Inputs:** Compare the performance of a PI
controller tuned by the formulas for minimum IAE, minimum

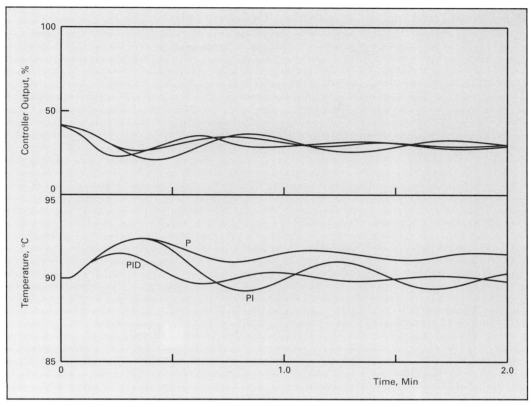

Fig. 4-2. Disturbance Response of P, PI, and PID Controllers Tuned for Quarter-Decay Ratio.

ISE, and minimum ITAE, for disturbance inputs. Use the steam heater parameters estimated by the tangent-and-point method.

The PI tuning parameters, using the formulas of Table 4-2 for IAE, Table 4-3 for ISE, and Table 4-4 for ITAE, and a process gain of 1%/%, time constant of 0.62 min, and dead time of 0.13 min, are:

	K_c, %/%	T_I, min
Minimum IAE	4.4	0.34
Minimum ISE	5.7	0.40
Minimum ITAE	3.8	0.32

The responses of the PI temperature controller for a 10°C step increase in inlet process temperature are shown in Fig. 4-3. For all practical purposes there is no difference between the three responses, because there is practically no difference between the tuning parameters. The ISE tuning produces a

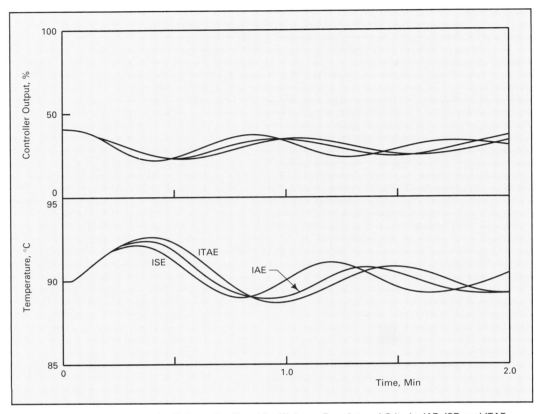

Fig. 4-3. Disturbance Response for PI Controller Tuned for Minimum Error Integral Criteria: IAE, ISE, and ITAE.

slightly faster response, but the error integral is only about 10% smaller than for the other two criteria. The minimum IAE tuning parameters and response are intermediate of the other two, but the overall differences between the three sets of tuning formulas are insignificant.

Example 4-3, Disturbance versus Set Point Tuning: Compare the performance of a series PID controller tuned by the formulas for minimum IAE on disturbance and set point inputs. Compare them for a disturbance input and for a set point change on the steam heater. Use the process parameters estimated by the tangent-and-point method.

The PID tuning formulas of Tables 4-2 and 4-5 allow the calculation of the minimum IAE tuning parameters on disturbance and set point inputs, but for the parallel PID controller. For a process gain of 1%/%, time constant of 0.62

min, and dead time of 0.13 min, the following parameters for the parallel PID controller are obtained:

Disturbance tuning:

$$K_c = 5.9\%/\% \qquad T_I = 0.22 \text{ min} \qquad T_D = 0.05 \text{ min}$$

Set point tuning:

$$K_c = 4.1\%/\% \qquad T_I = 0.87 \text{ min} \qquad T_D = 0.05 \text{ min}$$

These values can be converted to the tuning parameters for the equivalent series PID controller using the formulas presented in section 2-3. The results are:

	K_c', %/%	T_I', min	T_D', min
Disturbance tuning	3.8	0.14	0.08
Set point tuning	3.8	0.81	0.06

Notice that the only significant difference, in this case, is in the reset time, which is much longer for set point tuning than for the disturbance tuning.

The responses for a step change in disturbance, a 10°C increase in process inlet temperature, are compared in Fig. 4-4. The disturbance tuning results in a smaller maximum deviation and quicker return to set point, although the response is more oscillatory than for set point tuning. In this example, the IAE for the response for disturbance tuning is 64% of the IAE for set point tuning.

The responses for a 5°C step increase in set point are compared in Fig. 4-5. Notice that set point tuning results in very little overshoot and better overall approach to the new set point. In this case, the IAE for set point tuning is 48% of the IAE for disturbance tuning.

This example demonstrates that, as expected, each set of tuning formulas performs better than the other on the input for which it is intended.

The examples in this section have compared the tuning parameters obtained with the various sets of formulas

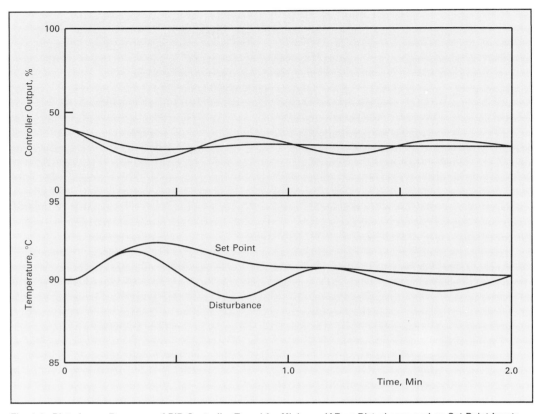

Fig. 4-4. Disturbance Response of PID Controller Tuned for Minimum IAE on Disturbance and on Set Point Inputs.

presented in previous sections of this unit and the performance of the controller when tuned by these methods. The results show that, for a process with the degree of uncontrollability of the heat exchanger (0.22), the use of derivative mode results in superior response. Also, for a given process, the quarter-decay ratio formulas and the various minimum error integral formulas for disturbance inputs result in tuning parameters that are similar.

4-4. Practical Controller Tuning Tips

The following is a collection of tips that should be useful in making the controller tuning task more efficient and satisfying:

1. *Tune coarse, not fine.* The realization that the performance of a feedback controller is not sensitive to the precise adjustment of its tuning parameters significantly simplifies the tuning task. Faced with the infinite possible

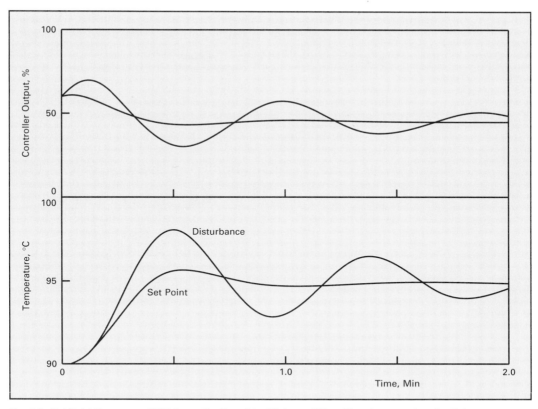

Fig. 4-5. Set Point Response of PID Controller Tuned for Minimum IAE on Disturbance and on Set Point.

combinations of precise tuning parameter values, one
might give up the task of tuning before even getting
started; but once it is realized that the controller
performance does not require precise setting of the tuning
parameters, the number of significantly different
combinations is reduced to a workable value. Also, there is
satisfaction in the large improvements in performance
achievable by coarse tuning, and frustration in the little
incremental improvement achievable by fine tuning. How
coarse? When tuning a controller, the author seldom
increases a parameter to less than twice or decreases it by
less than half its current value.

2. *Tune with confidence.* One of the reasons controller
performance is not sensitive to precise tuning parameter
settings is that any of the parameters may be adjusted to
make up for non-optimal values of the other parameters. A
successful approach is to select the integral time first, set
the derivative time to about one fourth of the integral time,
and then adjust the proportional gain to obtain tight control

of the controlled variable without undue variations in the
manipulated variable. If the response is still too oscillatory,
double the integral and derivative times; or, if it is too slow
in approaching the set point, halve the integral and
derivative times; then readjust the gain. When satisfactory
performance is obtained, LEAVE IT ALONE. DO NOT TRY
TO FINE TUNE IT FURTHER. Fine tuning it will result in
disappointment because of the insignificant incremental
improvement.

3. *Use all of the available information.* Enough information
   about the process equipment may be gathered to estimate
   the gain, time constant, and dead time of the process
   without having to resort to the open-loop step test (see
   sections 3-4 and 3-5). Information can also be gathered
   during trial-and-error tuning, which allows estimating the
   integral and derivative times from the period of oscillation
   of the loop or the total delay around the loop (dead time
   plus time constant). The latter can be estimated by the time
   difference between peaks in the controller output and the
   corresponding peaks in the transmitter signal.

4. *Try a longer integral time.* Poor loop response can many
   times be traced to trying to bring the controlled variable
   back to its set point faster than the process can respond.
   Increasing the integral time, in such cases, will allow
   increasing the process gain and improving the response.

5. *Tuning very controllable processes.* The tuning methods
   learned in Units 2 and 4 are not applicable to control loops
   with uncontrollability parameters less than 0.1. Such
   processes have very large ultimate gains that are difficult to
   determine by the closed-loop method of Unit 2. When the
   uncontrollability parameter is less than 0.1, the tuning
   formulas given in this unit result in very high gains and
   very fast reset times, which should not be used. What the
   formulas tell is that higher gains and faster reset times can
   be used than would reasonably be desired. In other words,
   it is a good idea to let good judgment override the
   formulas.

6. *Tuning very uncontrollable processes.* For processes with
   uncontrollability parameters of 1 and higher, it is important
   to recognize that even the optimally tuned feedback
   controller will result in poor performance such as large
   initial deviations on disturbance inputs and slow return to
   set point. In such cases, improved performance can be
   achieved through feedforward control (see Unit 8) and dead
   time compensation in the feedback controller (see Unit 6).

7. *Beware of problems that are not related to tuning.* The following problems interfere with the normal operation of a controller and, although they may appear to be tuning problems, they are not:

- Reset windup, caused by saturation of the controller output (see Unit 5)
- Interaction between loops (see Unit 9)
- Processes with inverse or overshoot response, caused by parallel effects of opposite direction between a process input and the controlled variable
- Changes in process parameters because of nonlinearities, which must be handled by adaptive control methods (see Unit 10)

All of these problems cause loss of feedback controller performance that must be handled by means other than controller tuning, such as, for example, decoupling, feedforward control, and adaptive control.

4-5. Summary

This unit has presented controller tuning formulas that are based on the gain, time constant, and dead time of the process in the feedback control loop, where ''process'' represents all of the elements between the controller output and its input. All of these formulas, whether they are intended to tune for quarter-decay ratio response or minimization of error integrals, result in controller parameter values that are about the same, particularly when it is realized that controller tuning need only be approximate rather than precise.

Exercises

4-1. *Based on the tuning formulas given in this unit, how must the controller gain be changed if, after the controller is tuned, the process gain were to double because of its nonlinear behavior?*

4-2. *How is the controllability of a feedback loop affected by the ratio of the process dead time to its time constant? How is it affected by the process gain?*

4-3. *Assuming that the quarter-decay ratio formulas of Table 4-1 give the same tuning parameters as those of Table*

2-1, what relationship can be established between the controller ultimate gain and the gain and uncontrollability parameter of the process in the loop? What is the relationship between the ultimate period and the process dead time?

4-4. *Compare the following processes as to controllability, sensitivity, and speed of response:*

	Process A	Process B	Process C
Gain	0.5%/%	2.0%/%	2.0%/%
Time constant	10 s	3 min	10 min
Dead time	5 s	1.5 min	2 min

4-5. *Calculate the quarter-decay ratio tuning parameters for the three processes of exercise 4-4 and a series PID controller.*

4-6. *Readjust the tuning parameters of exercise 4-5 if the PID controller is to be carried out with a processing period of 8 s on a computer control installation.*

4-7. *Repeat exercise 4-5 for a parallel PID controller tuned for minimum IAE on disturbance inputs.*

4-8. *Repeat exercise 4-5 for a parallel PID controller tuned for minimum IAE on set point changes.*

4-9. *Which criteria should be used to tune the slave controller in a cascade control system? In such a system the output of the master controller takes action by changing the set point of the slave controller.*

References

1. Lopez, A. M.; Murrill, P. W.; and Smith, C. L., "Controller Tuning Relationships Based on Integral Performance Criteria," *Instrumentation Technology*, V. 14 (Nov. 1967), p. 57.
2. Moore, C. F.; Smith, C. L.; and Murrill, P. W., "Simplifying Digital Control Dynamics for Controller Tuning and Hardware Lag Effects," *Instrument Practice*, V. 23 (Jan. 1969), p. 45.
3. Rovira, A. A., Ph.D. Dissertation, (Baton Rouge: Louisiana State University, 1981).
4. Ziegler, J. G., and Nichols, N. B., "Optimum Settings for Automatic Controllers," *Transactions ASME*, V. 64 (Nov. 1942), p. 759.

Unit 5:
How To Select Feedback Controller Modes

UNIT 5

How To Select Feedback Controller Modes

The preceding units have explained the tuning of proportional, proportional-integral, and proportional-integral-derivative feedback controllers. This unit will describe how to select which combination of the three basic controller modes should be used on various process control loops. A method called "controller synthesis" will guide in the selection of controller modes. The method will also give a new, simpler way to tune the controller. The most common types of control loops (level, pressure, flow, temperature, and composition) will be examined in the light of the guidelines given by the controller synthesis method.

Learning Objectives — When you have completed this unit you should:

A. Be able to decide whether the control objective is to maintain the controlled variable at the set point or within an acceptable range.

B. Know when to select proportional, integral, and derivative modes in specific control loops.

C. Be able to design and tune simple feedback controllers for level, pressure, flow, temperature, and composition.

D. Recognize the symptoms of "reset windup" and know how to prevent it.

5-1. Deciding on the Control Objective

Although the most common objective for feedback control is "to maintain the controlled variable at its set point," in some control situations (often in the control of level or pressure) it is acceptable to merely "maintain the controlled variable in an acceptable range." The differentiation between these two objectives is important, because, as was shown in Unit 2, the purpose of the integral mode is to eliminate the offset or steady-state error (maintain the controlled variable at the set point). Consequently, integral mode is not required when it is acceptable to allow the controlled variable to vary within a range. Eliminating the integral mode allows the use of higher proportional gain to reduce the initial deviation of the controlled variable caused by disturbances.

Two situations when the controlled variable can be allowed to vary in a range are:

- when the process is so controllable—a single long time constant with insignificant dead time—that the proportional gain can be set high and maintain the controlled variable in a very narrow range; and
- when it is desirable to allow the controlled variable to vary over a wide range.

The first of these situations calls for proportional (P) and proportional-derivative (PD) controllers with very high gains and for on-off controllers. It is found in the control of level in evaporators and reboilers and in the control of temperature in refrigeration systems, ovens, constant-temperature baths, and air conditioning/heating systems. On-off controllers can be used when the time constant is long enough that the cycling is of a very slow frequency; otherwise, proportional controllers are used to modulate the operation of the manipulated variable. In either case, the dead band of the on-off controller or the proportional band of the proportional controllers can be set very narrow. Derivative mode can be added to compensate for the lag in the sensor or final control element and, thus, improve stability.

The second situation calls for proportional controllers with as wide a proportional band as possible. It is found in the control of level in intermediate storage tanks and condenser accumulators and in the control of pressure in gas surge tanks.

5-2. Level and Pressure Control

Level and pressure are controlled either to keep them constant because of their effect on process or equipment operation or to smooth out variations in flow while satisfying the material balance. The former calls for "tight" control, while the latter is usually known as "averaging" control. Pressure is to gas systems what level is to liquid systems, although liquid pressure is sometimes controlled.

Tight Control

Two examples of tight liquid level control and one example of tight pressure control are shown in Fig. 5-1. The control of level in natural circulation evaporators and reboilers is

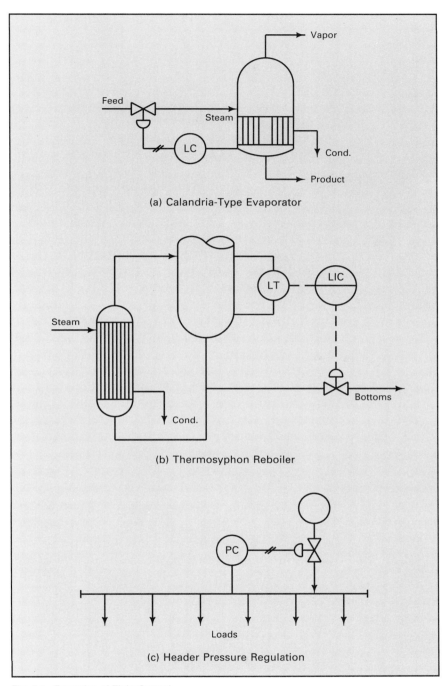

(a) Calandria-Type Evaporator

(b) Thermosyphon Reboiler

(c) Header Pressure Regulation

Fig. 5-1. Examples of Tight Control.

important because too low a level causes deposits on the bare hot tubes, while too high a level causes elevation of the boiling point, which reduces the heat transfer rate and prevents the formation of bubbles that enhance heat transfer by promoting turbulence. The example of tight pressure control or pressure regulation is the control of the pressure in a liquid or gas supply header, which must be maintained constant to prevent disturbances to the users when there is a sudden change in the demand of one or more of the users.

The design of tight level and pressure control systems requires a fast-acting control valve with a positioner, if necessary, to avoid secondary time lags, which would make the loop less controllable and cause oscillatory behavior at high controller gains. If the level or pressure controller is cascaded to a flow controller, the latter must be tuned as tight as possible (flow control is discussed in a later section of this unit).

The tight controller needs only proportional action with the gain set high—from 10 to over 100 (proportional band of 1% to 10% of range). If the lag of the level or pressure sensor were significant, derivative mode could be added to compensate for it and to afford a higher gain. The derivative time should be set approximately equal to the time constant of the sensor (see next section). Integral mode should not be used, as it would require a reduction of the proportional gain.

Averaging Level Control

Two examples of averaging level control are shown in Fig. 5-2: the control of level in a surge (or intermediate storage) tank and in a condenser accumulator drum. In these situations the liquid level in the tank has absolutely no effect on the operation of the process. It is important to realize that the purpose of an averaging level controller is to smooth out flow variations while keeping the tank from overflowing or running empty. If the level were to be controlled tight in such a situation, the outlet flow would vary just as much as the inlet flow(s), and it would be as if the tank (or accumulator) were not there.

The averaging level controller should be proportional-only with a set point of 50% of range, a gain of 1.0 (proportional band of 100%), and an output bias of 50%. This causes the outlet valve to be fully opened when the level is at 100% of

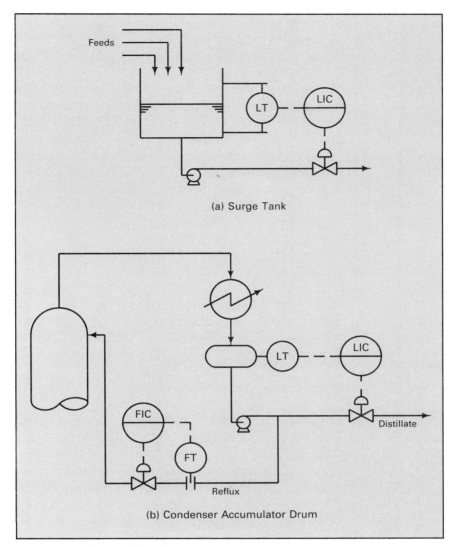

(a) Surge Tank

(b) Condenser Accumulator Drum

Fig. 5-2. Averaging Level Control.

range and fully closed when the level is at 0% of range, using the full capacity of the valve and of the tank. A higher gain would reduce the effective capacity of the tank for smoothing variations in flow, while a lower gain would reduce the effective capacity of the control valve and create the possibility of the tank overflowing or running dry. With the proposed design, the tank behaves as a low-pass filter to flow variations with a filter time constant of:

$$\tau_f = \frac{A(h_{max} - h_{min})}{K_c F_{max}} \qquad (5\text{-}1)$$

where A is the cross-sectional area of the tank in ft^2; h_{min} and h_{max} are, respectively, the low and high points of the range of the level transmitter in ft; and F_{max} is the maximum flow through the control valve when fully opened (100% controller output) or, if the level controller is cascaded to a flow controller, the upper limit of the flow transmitter range in ft^3/min. K_c is the controller gain in %/%, assumed to be 1.0 in this design. Notice that an increase in gain results in a reduction of the filter time constant and, therefore, less smoothing of the flow. A good way to see it is to notice that doubling the gain would be equivalent to reducing either the tank area or the transmitter range by a factor of 2, thus reducing the effective capacity of the tank. On the other hand, reducing the controller gain to half would be equivalent to reducing the capacity of the valve by half, thus increasing the possibility of the tank overflowing.

Averaging pressure control is not as common as averaging level control because, in the case of gas systems, a simple fixed resistance on the outlet of the surge tank is all that is required to smooth out variations in flow.

Intermediate Level Control

In some intermediate situations that do not require a very tight level control, it is important not to allow the level to swing the full range of the transmitter (as in averaging level control). A typical example would be a blending tank, where the level controls the tank volume and, therefore, the residence time for blending. If a $\pm 5\%$ variation in residence time is acceptable, a proportional controller with a gain of 5 to 10 or even lower could be used, as the flow would not be expected to vary the full range of the control valve capacity.

This section has presented several examples of control situations where integral mode is not required. In the rest of this unit it will be assumed that the objective is to maintain the controlled variable at its set point, and, therefore, integral mode is required on the feedback controller.

5-3. Controller Synthesis

The concept of controller synthesis was applied independently by Dahlin (Reference 1) and Higham (Reference 2) to design computer-based controllers with dead time compensation.

(Dahlin's design will be examined in detail in a later unit).
The idea was extended by Martin, et al., (Reference 3) to
select the modes and tune continuous controllers. Later,
Rivera, et al., (Reference 4) used a different type of block
diagram analysis known as "Internal Model Control" to arrive
at the same results as Martin and to extend them.

Basically, the idea is to derive a formula to synthesize the
feedback controller from an algebraic analysis of the general
block diagram of the feedback control loop shown in Fig. 5-3.
In this simplified two-block diagram, one block stands for the
controller, $G_c(s)$, and the other one for the "process," $G(s)$, the
latter representing the combined dynamic response of the
control valve, the process proper, and the sensor/transmitter.
From block diagram algebra, the closed-loop response of the
controlled variable, $C(s)$, to the set point, $R(s)$, is given by:

$$\frac{C(s)}{R(s)} = \frac{G_c(s)G(s)}{1 + G_c(s)G(s)} \qquad (5\text{-}2)$$

As in Unit 2, the operator "s" stands for the "rate of change"
operator. Its presence in the transfer functions indicates that
they include dynamic effects (lags and dead times). The
general "controller synthesis formula" is obtained by simply
solving for $G_c(s)$ from Eq. (5-2):

$$G_c(s) = \frac{1}{G(s)} \frac{C(s)/R(s)}{1 - C(s)/R(s)} \qquad (5\text{-}3)$$

Notice that the synthesized controller is the combination of
two parts, one part to compensate for the process transfer
function, $G(s)$, and the other to obtain a specified closed-loop
response of the controlled variable to the set point, $C(s)/R(s)$.
In other words, different controllers could be obtained for the
same process by specifying different closed-loop responses,

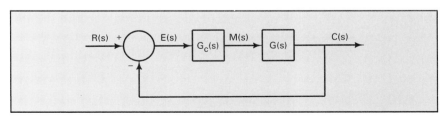

Fig. 5-3. Block Diagram of the General Feedback Control Loop.

and different controllers for different process transfer functions for the same closed-loop response specification.

Equation (5-3) shows that "perfect control" (that is, having the controlled variable always equal to the set point [C(s)/R(s) = 1]) is not possible because it would require a controller with infinite gain. This is reassuring, because the formula could not be trusted if it stated otherwise.

For the closed-loop response, Dahlin (Reference 1) specified a first-order lag or low-pass filter response with an adjustable closed-loop time constant τ_c (or break-point frequency $\lambda = 1/\tau_c$). In its simplest form, when the process transfer function does not have dead time, the closed-loop transfer function becomes:

$$\frac{C(s)}{R(s)} = \frac{1}{\tau_c s + 1} \qquad (5\text{-}4)$$

The steady-state gain of this transfer function is 1, assuring the absence of offset and thus introducing integral mode into the synthesized controller. The closed-loop time constant τ_c can be adjusted to shape the response of the loop: the smaller τ_c the tighter (faster) the controlled response. τ_c provides a convenient parameter to reach a compromise between fast approach to set point and acceptable variations in the controller output. In this sense it can considered a "performance adjustment" parameter.

Substituting Eq. (5-4) into Eq. (5-3) and simplifying, the Dahlin synthesis formula for processes without dead time is obtained:

$$G_c(s) = \frac{1}{G(s)} \frac{1}{\tau_c s} \qquad (5\text{-}5)$$

This formula will be used in the rest of this section to select controller modes for various process transfer functions. Notice that the presence of the operator s in the denominator of the controller transfer function means that the controller has integral mode. This is a direct result of the specification of unity gain in the closed-loop response specification.

The following paragraphs show what controller modes result from the synthesis formula, Eq. (5-5), for different process transfer functions.

Fast Process

If the process is fast compared to the desired closed-loop response, the process transfer function is simply a gain:

$$G(s) = K \tag{5-6}$$

Substituting into Eq. (5-5), a pure integral controller results, with the following transfer function and suggested tuning:

$$G_c(s) = K_I/s \tag{5-7}$$

Tuning: $K_I = 1/(K\tau_c)$

In practice, the control of exit temperature in reformer furnaces and some flow control loops has been determined to be fast enough to require only pure integral control.

First-Order Process

Such processes can be represented by a first-order transfer function with no dead time:

$$G(s) = \frac{K}{\tau s + 1} \tag{5-8}$$

Substituting into Eq. (5-5) and rearranging, a proportional-integral (PI) controller results:

$$G_c(s) = K_c\left[1 + \frac{1}{T_I s}\right] \tag{5-9}$$

Tuning: $K_c = \tau/(K\tau_c)$ $T_I = \tau$

The tuning suggests that the integral time be set equal to the process time constant and that the gain be adjusted to obtain any desired loop performance.

In comparing the fast process to the first-order process, it is found that, given the specification of zero offset, integral mode is the basic controller mode and proportional is added to compensate for the process lag. This way of looking at the controller is different from the way it evolved in industrial practice, where proportional mode came first and integral was later added to eliminate offset.

Second-Order Process

If a second lag is present in the control loop (as, for example, the sensor/transmitter, the control valve actuator, or the jacket on a stirred tank), the process transfer function contains two lags:

$$G(s) = \frac{K}{(\tau_1 s + 1)(\tau_2 s + 1)} \qquad (5\text{-}10)$$

Substituting into Eq. (5-5) and rearranging, a series PID controller is obtained:

$$G_c(s) = K_c \left[1 + \frac{1}{T_I s} \right] [T_D s + 1] \qquad (5\text{-}11)$$

Tuning: $K_c = \tau_1/(K\tau_c)$ $T_I = \tau_1$ $T_D = \tau_2$

The tuning suggests that the integral time be set equal to one process time constant and the derivative time equal to the other, while the proportional gain is once again adjustable to obtain the desired tightness of response. In industrial practice, the integral time is always longer than the derivative time, but the synthesis procedure does not differentiate between the two time constants. Notice that the synthesis formula does not suggest the lag in the derivative unit that is required to make it realizable [see Eq. (2-10)].

The result of controller synthesis is that derivative mode be added to compensate for the second lag in the process transfer function. This suggestion is consistent with the common practice of applying the three-mode controller to temperature control loops, because in these loops the sensor lag is significant.

Integrating Processes

An integrating process has a transfer function with an s in the denominator:

$$G(s) = \frac{K}{s(\tau s + 1)} \qquad (5\text{-}12)$$

Substituting into Eq. (5-5) and simplifying, a proportional-derivative (PD) controller is obtained:

$$G_c(s) = K_c(T_D s + 1) \qquad (5-13)$$

Tuning: $K_c = 1/(K\tau_c)$ $T_D = \tau$

The tuning suggests that the derivative time be set equal to the process time constant and that the process gain be adjustable to the desired tightness of control. Once again, the required lag on the derivative unit is not present in the synthesized controller but must be included in the actual implementation. Although the proportional controller does not have offset for changes in set point, disturbances cause offset because the controller does not have integral mode.

Liquid level control is the only common continuous process with an integrating tranfer function. As stated in the preceding section, proportional controllers are indicated for such processes when other loop lags are negligible. Derivative mode would be added to compensate for any significant lag in the sensor, process, or control valve.

Processes with Inverse or Overshoot Response

Some processes exhibit a response that either starts in the opposite direction of or overshoots the final steady-state change. Typical examples of such "inverse or overshoot" responses are shown in Fig. 5-4. They result when the manipulated variable has two parallel effects of opposite direction on the controlled variable. The transfer functions of these processes show a negative lead term and two regular lag terms:

$$G(s) = \frac{K(1 - \tau_3 s)}{(\tau_1 s + 1)(\tau_2 s + 1)} \qquad (5-14)$$

Were this transfer function substituted into Eq. (5-5), the result would be a controller transfer function with a negative or unstable lag term, which would not be advisable to use because the stability of the loop should not depend on exact compensation of the process transfer function. However, this

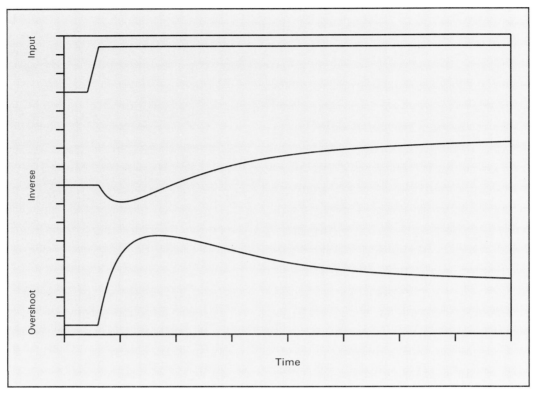

Fig. 5-4. Inverse and Overshoot Response to a Step Input.

problem can be avoided by specifying that the closed-loop response transfer function contain the negative lead term:

$$\frac{C(s)}{R(s)} = \frac{1 - \tau_3 s}{\tau_c s + 1}$$

(5-15)

Substituting Eqs. (5-14) and (5-15) into Eq. (5-3) and rearranging, a series PID controller with the following transfer function and tuning formulas results:

$$G_c(s) = K_c\left[1 + \frac{1}{T_I s}\right][T_D s + 1]$$

(5-16)

Tuning: $K_c = \dfrac{\tau_1}{K(\tau_c + \tau_3)}$ $T_I = \tau_1$ $T_D = \tau_2$

Comparison of Eqs. (5-11) and (5-16) shows that the only difference in the controller for the standard second-order process is in the tuning of the controller gain. The presence of the negative lead term in the process transfer function forces the use of smaller gain than for the regular second-order process. This gain reduction makes sense, given that a process with inverse or overshoot response would be less controllable than a process with regular response.

Inverse responses have been observed in distillation columns and exothermic chemical reactors. They can also occur as the result of interaction between control loops, as will be seen in Unit 9.

Processes with Dead Time

Recall from Unit 3 that many process responses can be approximated with a first-order plus dead time transfer function:

$$G(s) = \frac{Ke^{-tos}}{\tau s + 1} \tag{5-17}$$

If the process has dead time, then it cannot be specified that the closed-loop responses start before the process dead time, because that would require the controller to take action before an error is detected. As in the previous case, the closed-loop specification must be modified. This time the modification is to include the process dead time in the closed-loop response:

$$\frac{C(s)}{R(s)} = \frac{e^{-tos}}{\tau_c s + 1} \tag{5-18}$$

Substituting Eqs. (5-17) and (5-18) into Eq. (5-3), the following controller transfer function results:

$$Gc(s) = \frac{\tau s + 1}{K} \frac{1}{\tau_c s + 1 - e^{-tos}} \tag{5-19}$$

This is the result Dahlin (Reference 1) used to design a control algorithm with compensation for process dead time; but, as dead time compensation requires the use of computer memory, its discussion is deferred to Unit 6. Nevertheless, Eq. (5-19) can be put in the form of a series PID controller if the dead time is approximated with a first-order Padé approximation (see Reference 5 for details). The resulting controller transfer function and tuning are:

$$G_c(s) = K_c \left[1 + \frac{1}{T_I s} \right] \frac{T_D s + 1}{\alpha T_D s + 1} \qquad (5\text{-}20)$$

Tuning:

$$K_c = \frac{\tau}{K(\tau_c + t_0)} \qquad T_I = \tau \qquad T_D = t_0/2 \qquad \alpha = \frac{\tau_c}{\tau_c + t_0}$$

The tuning formulas suggest that the integral time be set equal to the process time constant, the derivative time equal to one half the dead time (just as in the quarter-decay ratio formulas of Table 4-1), and the proportional gain be adjusted to achieve the desired degree of tightness of the closed-loop response. The dead time appears in the denominator of the gain formula, showing that the longer the dead time the smaller the gain (as is suggested by all the tuning formulas of Unit 4).

In this case the synthesis formula suggests a filter for the derivative unit, but it also suggests a formula for the filter parameter α. In practice such a parameter is not adjustable.

Practical Conclusions

In summary, the following practical conclusions can be drawn from the controller synthesis approach:

1. A pure integral controller is indicated for very fast processes, with proportional mode added to compensate for the major process time constant and with derivative mode added to compensate for the second time constant or dead time.
2. A simple tuning procedure is to set the integral time equal to the major process time constant and the derivative time equal to the second time constant or one half the dead time, and to adjust the controller gain to obtain the desired closed-loop response. This reduces the tuning procedure to the adjustment of a single performance parameter when the time constants and dead time are known.
3. For processes with inverse or overshoot response, there is an upper limit to the process gain, obtained by setting $\tau_c = 0$ in the tuning formula:

$$K_{cmax} = \frac{\tau}{K\tau_3} \qquad (5\text{-}21)$$

Similarly, for processes with dead time, the upper limit on the gain is given by:

$$K_{cmax} = \frac{\tau}{Kt_0} \qquad (5\text{-}22)$$

4. For integrating processes, such as liquid level controllers, pure proportional or proportional-derivative controllers are indicated, with the derivative time set to the process time constant if it is significant. The gain is adjustable for this controller also, but offset will result for disturbance inputs.

Example 5-1, Controller Tuning for Steam Heater Using Synthesis: Determine the controller tuning parameters for the steam heater temperature control loop of Fig. 3-1, and compare them with those obtained by the quarter-decay ratio and minimum IAE criteria of Unit 4.

As the process transfer function is first-order plus dead time, controller synthesis would recommend a series PID controller. The process parameters were determined in Example 3-2 using the tangent-and-point method, that is:

$$\text{Gain} = 1\%/\% \qquad \text{Time constant} = 0.62 \text{ min}$$

$$\text{Dead time} = 0.13 \text{ min}$$

The following table compares the tuning parameters for a series PID controller, using Table 4-1 for quarter-decay ratio, the results of Example 4-3 for the minimum IAE parameters, and the tuning formulas of Eq. (5-20) with $\tau_c = 0$ (maximum gain) for the synthesis method:

	K_c', %/%	T_I', min	T_D', min
Quarter-Decay Ratio	5.6	0.27	0.07
Minimum IAE Disturbance	3.8	0.14	0.08
Minimum IAE Set Point	3.8	0.81	0.06
Synthesis	4.6	0.62	0.07

Once again it is evident that the tuning by all three methods is similar, with synthesis producing parameters that are intermediate between the quarter-decay ratio and minimum IAE set point tuning formulas.

Figure 5-5 shows the response of the heater outlet temperature to a 5°C raise in set point using the four sets of tuning

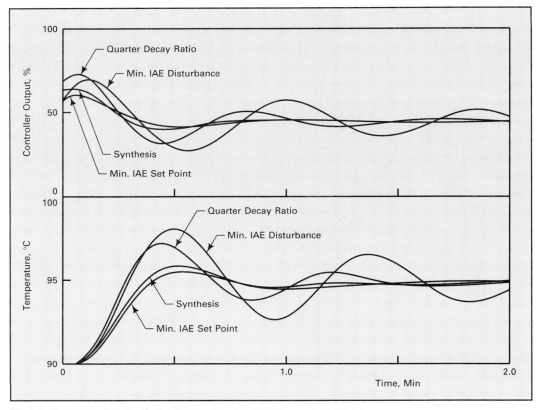

Fig. 5-5. **Response of Heater Outlet Temperature to a 5°C Change in Set Point.**

parameters. Notice that the synthesis response and the minimum IAE set point response are more conservative than the other two.

In this section the controller synthesis method has been used to arrive at guidelines for selecting feedback controller modes. In the sections that follow some specific control loops will be examined.

5-4. Flow Control

Flow control is the simplest and most common of the feedback control loops. A schematic diagram of a flow control loop is shown in Fig. 5-6, showing that the process is simply the control valve. Although there are several different types of flow sensors (orifice, venturi, flow tubes, magnetic flowmeters, turbine meters, etc.), most of them are very fast; the most

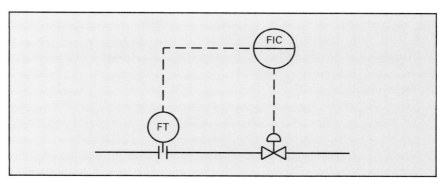

Fig. 5-6. Typical Flow Control Loop.

significant lag in the loop is usually the control valve actuator with a time constant of a few seconds.

As flow is such a fast loop, the synthesis method would suggest a pure integral controller. In practice, flow controllers have been tuned with proportional gains less than unity and very fast integral times (of the order of seconds), which is essentially a pure integral controller. Such an approach is acceptable when flow is controlled to maintain a constant rate with few manual changes in flow set point.

However, when the flow controller is the slave in a cascade control scheme, it is important for the flow to respond fast to set point changes. This requires a proportional-integral controller with a gain of one or higher, which, to maintain stability, may require an increase in the integral time from the few seconds normally used in flow controllers. The synthesis formulas suggest that the reset time be set equal to the time constant of the loop (usually that of the control valve actuator) and that the gain be adjusted for the desired tightness of control. In cascade situations, tight flow control is indicated.

The proportional gain should also be increased when hysteresis of the control valve causes variations in the flow around its set point. Hysteresis is caused by static friction in the valve stem, which creates a difference between the actual valve position and the corresponding controller output. The error changes direction according to the direction that the stem must move, and this causes a dead band around the desired valve position. Increasing the flow controller gain reduces the amplitude of the flow variations caused by hysteresis. Valve positioners also reduce hysteresis and speed up valves, but they are usually difficult to justify for flow control loops.

5-5. Temperature Control

Temperature controllers are usually proportional-integral-derivative (PID) (the derivative mode is required to compensate for the lag of the temperature sensor, which is usually significant). The synthesis formulas suggest that the derivative time be set equal to the sensor time constant, which can be estimated by the following formula:

$$\tau_s = \frac{MC_p}{hA} \tag{5-23}$$

where M is the mass of the sensor, including the thermowell, in lb; C_p is the specific heat, in Btu/lb-°F; h is the film coefficient of heat transfer, in Btu/min-ft^2-°F; and A is the area of the thermowell, in ft^2. When these units are used, the time constant is calculated in minutes.

Temperature is the variable most often controlled in chemical reactors, furnaces, and heat exchangers. When the temperature controller manipulates the flow of steam or fuel to a heater or furnace, the rate of heat is proportional to the flow of steam or fuel. This is because the heat of condensation of the steam and the heating value of the fuel remain approximately constant with load. However, when the manipulated variable is cooling water or a hot oil, as in Fig. 5-7a, the heat rate is very nonlinear with water or oil flow, because the heat transfer rate requires that the outlet utility temperature get closer to its inlet temperature as the heat transfer rate increases. This means that it requires higher increments in flow for equal increments in heat rate as the load increases. Because of this and other problems with excessive water temperature at low heat transfer rate, a preferred way to control heat exchangers is to maintain a constant coolant rate and bypass some of the process fluid around the exchanger, as shown in Fig. 5-7b. This scheme also removes the exchanger lag from the temperature control loop, resulting in faster control.

Example 5-2, Estimate of Temperature Sensor Time Constant: Estimate the time constant of an RTD (resistance temperature device) weighing 0.5 lb and having a specific heat of 0.033 Btu/lb-°F. The thermowell is cylindrical with an outside

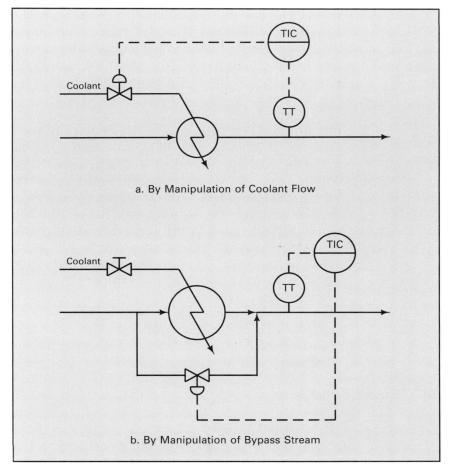

a. By Manipulation of Coolant Flow

b. By Manipulation of Bypass Stream

Fig. 5-7. Temperature Control.

diameter of 0.5 in. and a length of 5 in. The film coefficient of heat transfer between the fluid and the thermowell is 90 Btu/h-ft²-°F. The area of the thermowell is: $3.1416(0.5)(5)/144 = 0.055$ ft². The time constant, from Eq. (5-23) is estimated as:

$$(0.5)(0.033)/(90/60)(0.055) = 0.20 \text{ min}$$

5-6. Analyzer Control

The major problem with the control of composition is usually associated with the sensor/transmitter. Sampling of process streams introduces significant dead time into the loop, as well as some measurement noise if the sample is not representative due to poor mixing. Sensors are usually slow, and their measurements are sensitive to temperature and other process variables. In the case of analyzers for hydrocarbon mixtures, they are usually done by chromatographic separation, which is discontinuous in time. They also have a time delay in the measurement of the order of the analysis cycle, compounding the control problem.

In spite of all the sources for time delays in the sampling and analysis, it must be kept in mind that the important parameter is the ratio of the dead time to the process time constant. If the combination of the analysis sample time and the time delay is less than the process time constant, a proportional-integral-derivative controller is indicated. Any of the tuning formulas can be used to tune it, but the synthesis formulas have an advantage over the others: they can be extrapolated to any value of the dead time-to-time constant ratio. On the other hand, if a total dead time and sample time is of the order of several time constants, the situation is effectively the same as that of a fast process, and a pure integral controller is suggested by controller synthesis. This is because the process is fast relative to the time frame in which it can be measured. This point will be discussed further in Unit 6.

5-7. Reset Windup

The problem of reset windup or saturation of the controller output is one that may often be considered a tuning problem when, in reality, it cannot be resolved by tuning the controller. It is, therefore, important to be able to recognize the symptoms of reset windup and to know how to resolve them.

A properly tuned controller will behave well as long as its output remains in a range where it can change the manipulated flow. However, it will behave poorly if, for any reason, the effect of the controller output on the manipulated flow is lost. A gap between the limit on the controller output and the operational limit of the control valve is the most common cause of reset windup. The symptom is a large overshoot of the controlled variable while the integral mode in the controller is crossing the gap. Reset windup occurs most commonly during start-up and shutdown, but it can also occur during product grade switches and large disturbances during continuous operation. Momentary loss of a pump may also cause reset windup.

To illustrate a typical occurrence of reset windup, consider the temperature control of a large reactor by manipulation of steam flow to the jacket, as sketched in Fig. 5-8a. Assume that the reactor is poorly insulated and operating close to full capacity, with the steam valve at 95% open. At point ''a'' in the trend recording of Fig. 5-8b, a sudden thunderstorm causes a sharp drop in the reactor temperature, which causes the steam valve to open fully. However, because the controller output is not properly limited, it continues to increase beyond the 100% valve position (20-mA output) to the full supply current of 125% (24 mA). The gap mentioned before is the controller output range between 100 and 125%, over which the valve does not move because it is held against its fully opened position of 100%. At point ''b'' in the trend the

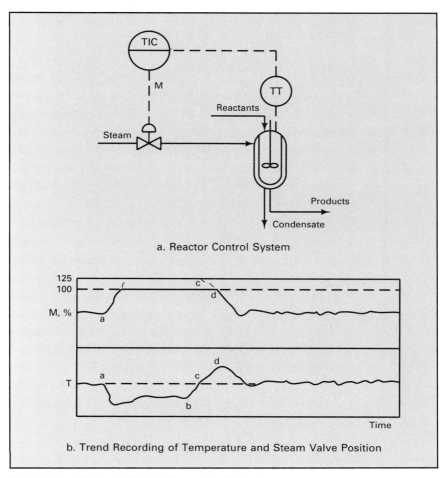

a. Reactor Control System

b. Trend Recording of Temperature and Steam Valve Position

Fig. 5-8. Reset Windup in Reactor Temperature Control.

thunderstorm subsides, and the reactor temperature starts to increase back to its set point. However, when it reaches its set point (at point ''c''), the controller output is still at 125% of range and the valve is fully opened. At this point the integral mode starts to reduce the controller output, but, because it is in the gap, the control valve continues to be fully opened until the controller output reaches 100% at point ''d''. Meanwhile, the reactor temperature has continued to increase and its response shows the large overshoot symptomatic of reset windup. At point ''d'' the steam valve finally begins to close and the reactor temperature starts to decrease back to its set point.

Prevention of reset windup is based on eliminating any possible gaps over which the controller output does not have an effect on the manipulated flow. In this case it would require the setting of limits on the controller output that correspond to the limits on the control valve operation. These limits are not always 0 and 100% of range. For example, some control valves are poorly designed, and their installed characteristics may show little change in flow for valve positions above 80 or 90% open. In such cases the controller output limit should be set at the point where there is little increase in flow with an increase in controller output. Modern microprocessor-based controllers are equipped with adjustable limits on the output as well as on the set point, so there is no expense in setting the limits. The job is to determine what the limits should be.

5-8. Summary

This unit has presented the selecting of feedback controller modes for various typical process control loops and a simple way to tune controllers based on the controller synthesis method. Situations where proportional, pure integral, and proportional-derivative controllers are indicated (in addition to the usual two- and three-mode controllers) were discussed. The importance of recognizing situations where tight control is not desirable, and those where the controlled variable may be allowed to vary in a range, was stated. An example showed that it is also important to recognize the symptoms of reset windup so that they are not confused with controller tuning problems.

Exercises

5-1. When would you use tight level control, and when would you use averaging level control? In which of the two is it important to maintain the level at the set point? Give an example of each.

5-2. Briefly describe the technique of controller synthesis. Is it possible to synthesize a feedback controller for perfect control (that is, one that can keep the controlled variable at its set point at all times)?

5-3. What is the meaning of the "performance parameter" τ_c in Dahlin's closed-loop specification? How would you use it in tuning the synthesized controller? Which of the controller tuning parameters depends on the performance parameter?

5-4. For which process models can the synthesized controller be put in the form of a series PID controller? In each case, state the relationship between the integral and derivative times and the process model parameters.

5-5. For an integrating process, which modes of control are suggested by controller synthesis? Under which conditions can such a controller produce or not produce an offset?

5-6. When is a pure integral controller suggested by the controller synthesis procedure?

5-7. What type of controller is recommended by synthesis for flow control loops? Temperature loops? Composition loops?

5-8. Calculate the tuning parameters for quarter-decay ratio response, minimum IAE on disturbance, minimum IAE on set point, and synthesis for a process with a gain of 1%/%, a time constant of 1.0 min, and a dead time of (a) 0.01 min, (b) 0.3 min, and (c) 2.0 min. For the synthesis method, use $\tau_c = 0$ to calculate the maximum controller gain.

5-9. What is the typical symptom of reset windup? What causes it? How can it be prevented?

References

1. Dahlin, E. B., "Designing and Tuning Digital Controllers," *Instruments and Control Systems*, V. 41 (June 1968), p. 77.
2. Higham, J. D., "'Single-Term' Control of First- and Second-Order Processes with Dead Time," *Control* (Feb. 1968), pp. 136–140.
3. Martin, J., Jr.; Corripio, A. B.; and Smith, C. L., "How To Select Controller Modes and Tuning Parameters from Simple Process Models," *ISA Transactions*, V. 15 (Apr. 1976), pp. 314–319.
4. Rivera, D. E.; Morari, M.; and Skogestad, S., "Internal Model Control, 4. PID Controller Design," *Industrial and Engineering Chemistry Process Design and Development*, V. 25 (1986), p. 252.
5. Smith, C. A., and Corripio, A. B., *Principles and Practice of Automatic Process Control* (New York: Wiley, 1985).

Unit 6:
Computer Feedback Control

UNIT 6

Computer Feedback Control

Most process industries today use computers and microprocessors to carry out the basic feedback control calculations. Microprocessors carry out the control calculations in distributed control systems (DCS), programmable logic controllers (PLC), and single-loop controllers, while larger computers carry out higher-level control functions, many of which include feedback control. Unlike analog instruments, digital devices must sample the controlled variable and compute and update the controller output at discrete intervals of time. This unit looks at discrete feedback control algorithms, the effect of sampling, and adjusting the controller tuning parameters to compensate for it. Included are some tuning formulas specifically designed for discrete controllers and a controller that compensates for process dead time.

Learning Objectives — When you have completed this unit you should:

A. Be able to differentiate between parallel and series PID control algorithms.

B. Know how to correct the controller tuning parameters for the effect of sampling in digital feedback control.

C. Understand the issues involved in selecting the sampling time or processing frequency for digital control loops.

D. Be able to tune computer and microprocessor-based feedback controllers.

E. Apply feedback controllers with dead time compensation.

6-1. Feedback Control Algorithms

The formulas that are programmed to calculate the controller output are discrete versions of the transfer functions of the feedback controllers presented in Unit 2. A particular way to arrange a formula for the calculation is called an ''algorithm''. This section presents the ''position'' and ''velocity'' PID algorithms, the latter being the most commonly used in computer and microprocessor controllers. As there is no extra cost in programming all three modes of control, most algorithms contain all three and then use flags and logic to allow the control engineer to specify any single mode or a combination of two or three modes.

As the feedback control calculation is made at regular intervals of time, the controlled variable or "process variable" (PV) is sampled only when the controller output is calculated and updated, as illustrated in Fig. 6-1. Notice that the controller output is updated at the sampling instants and held constant for one sampling interval, T. The sampling of the process variable is done by the analog-to-digital converter (ADC) and multiplexer (MUX), while the updating and holding of the controller output is done by the digital-to-analog converter (DAC).

The calculation of the error for a reverse-acting controller is done simply by subtracting the process variable from its set point:

$$E_k = R_k - C_k \qquad (6\text{-}1)$$

where E_k is the error, R_k is the set point, C_k is the process or controlled variable. The subscript "k" stands for the kth sample or calculation of the algorithm. For a direct-acting controller the signs of the process variable and the set point are reversed, or, alternatively, the controller gain is set to a negative value.

Unit 2 established that there are two transfer functions for the PID controller: the parallel version, Eq. (2-9), and the series

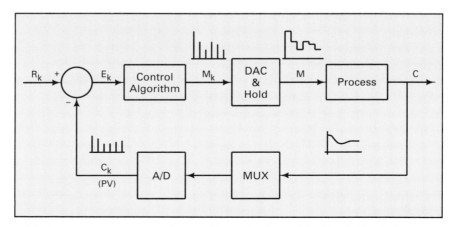

Fig. 6-1. Block Diagram of a Computer Feedback Control Loop Showing the Sampled Nature of the Signals.

version, Eq. (2-10). The formulas to convert the tuning parameters from one version to the other were given in Unit 2. Although the series version is the one used in analog controllers, many computer controllers use the parallel version, and some computer control systems allow the option of either version.

Parallel Position PID Algorithm

Discretization of the transfer function of the parallel controller, Eq. (2-9), results in the following formulas for the parallel version of the algorithm:

$$M_k = M_0 + K_c [E_k + (T/T_I)S_k + (T_D/T) (E_k - E_{k-1})] \quad (6\text{-}2)$$

where:

$$S_k = S_{k-1} + E_k$$
M_k = the controller output at sample k
M_0 = the initial controller output
S_k = the sum of the error
T = the sample time or interval between controller updates

Notice that the "discretization" of the continuous PID controller consists of replacing the integral term with the sum of the errors and the derivative term with the difference between the last two errors.

Parallel Velocity PID Algorithm

A more efficient way to program the PID algorithm, from the standpoints of handling the initialization when the controller is switched from "manual" to "automatic" and of limiting the controller output to prevent reset windup (see section 5-6), is the velocity algorithm. It is obtained by taking the difference between the applications of Eq. (6-2) for two consecutive samples:

$$\Delta M_k = K_c[E_k - E_{k-1} + (T/T_I)E_k + (T_D/T) (E_k - 2E_{k-1}$$
$$+ E_{k-2})]$$
$$M_k = M_{k-1} + \Delta M_k \qquad\qquad (6\text{-}3)$$

Notice that in the velocity algorithm the controller output can be directly limited, while in the position algorithm the error sum must be limited to prevent windup. Initialization of the velocity algorithm requires only that the controller output be set to its initial value once, while on the position algorithm the initial value is used in the calculation at every sample. For these reasons the velocity algorithm is more commonly used than the position algorithm. The two algorithms are merely two algebraic rearrangements of the same formula and should produce exactly the same results.

Series Velocity PID Algorithm

Discretization of the series version of the three-mode controller, Eq. (2-10), results in the following algorithm, already in velocity form:

$$\Delta M_k = K_c' [Y_k - Y_{k-1} + (T/T_I')Y_k] \qquad (6\text{-}4)$$

where $Y_k = E_k + (T_D'/T) (E_k - E_{k-1})$.

The quantity Y is the output of the "proportional-plus-derivative" part of the formula, which is in series with the "proportional-plus-integral" part.

The parameters of the series PID algorithm are related (but not identical) to those of the parallel version. However, Eqs. (2-11) and (2-12) allow converting between the tuning parameters of one version and the other.

Practical Implementation of the PID Algorithm

The PID algorithm formulas presented so far are those found in most textbooks. However, were they to be used to control actual processes, the derivative term would tend to produce undesirable pulses on set point changes. Pulses will also result from the discretization of transmitter signals into digital numbers of limited resolution. There are two simple remedies to these pulses: have the derivative act on the process variable instead of the error, and introduce a filter that limits the dynamic gain of the derivative term.

It is seldom desirable for the derivative mode of the controller to respond to set point changes, because set point changes cause large changes in the error that last for only one sample. When the derivative mode acts on the error, as in the algorithms of Eqs. (6-2), (6-3), and (6-4), undesirable pulses or "derivative kicks" occur on the controller output right after the set point is changed. These pulses, which last for one sampling interval, can be avoided by having the derivative mode act on the process variable rather than on the error. For the parallel velocity algorithm, Eq. (6-3) is modified as follows for implementation in computer- and microprocessor-based controllers:

Parallel velocity algorithm without derivative kick:

$$\Delta M_k = K_c[E_k - E_{k-1} + (T/T_I)E_k + B_k] \qquad (6\text{-}5)$$

where $B_k = \dfrac{\alpha T_D}{T + \alpha T_D} B_{k-1} - \dfrac{T_D}{T + \alpha T_D} (C_k - 2C_{k-1} + C_{k-2})$.

In this formula the minus sign is used on the assumption that the algorithm is reverse-acting; for a direct-acting controller, the sign would be positive, because then the error would be the process variable minus the set point.

For the series algorithm, Eq. (6-4) must be modified as follows:

Series velocity algorithm without derivative kick:

$$\Delta M_k = K_c' [E_k - E_{k-1} + (T/T_I')E_k] \qquad (6\text{-}6)$$

where

$$E_k = R_k - Y_k$$

$$Y_k = \frac{\alpha T_D'}{T + \alpha T_D'} Y_{k-1}$$

$$+ \frac{T}{T + \alpha T_D'} C_k + \frac{(\alpha + 1) T_D'}{T + \alpha T_D'} (C_k - C_{k-1})$$

For a direct-acting controller, the terms in the calculation of the error are swapped.

In Eqs. (6-5) and (6-6) the filter parameter "α" has a very special meaning. Its reciprocal "$1/\alpha$" is the amplification factor on the change of the error at each sampling instant (also called the "dynamic gain limit"). Notice that, for the algorithms without the noise filter, the amplification factor on

the change in error has no limit. For example, if the sampling
interval is one second and the derivative time is one minute,
the change in error at each sample is multiplied by a factor of
60. By setting the nonadjustable parameter "α" to a
reasonable value, say 0.1, the algorithm designer can assure
that the change in error cannot be amplified by a factor greater
than 10, independent of the sampling interval and the
derivative time. The dynamic limit is also to the advantage of
the control engineer, because it allows him or her to set the
derivative time to any desired value without danger of
introducing large undesirable pulses on the controller output.

Most modern computer- and microprocessor-based controllers
provide the option of having the derivative mode act on the
error or on the process variable; the algorithm usually defaults
to the second option unless the first one is specified.

Example 6-1, Response of the Derivative Unit to a Ramp:
Calculate the output of the derivative term on the derivative
unit of the series velocity algorithm to a ramp that starts at
zero and increases by 1% each sample. Use a sample time of 1
s and a derivative time of 0.5 min. The filter parameter is 0.1.

Direct substitution of the values given and of the process
variable at each sample into Eq. (6-6) produces the results
summarized in the table below. The results for the "ideal"
derivative unit are calculated using a filter parameter of zero.

Sample	0	1	2	3	4	5	.. 10	.. 20	.. 40
C_k	0	1	2	3	4	5	.. 10	.. 20	.. 40
Y_k	0	8.5	15.2	20.3	24.5	27.9	.. 38.3	.. 49.9	.. 70.0
Ideal	30	31.0	32.0	33.0	34.0	35.0	.. 40.0	.. 50.0	.. 70.0

Notice that the ideal derivative unit without filter jumps to 30
at time 0 and increments by 1 each sample. Both these
responses are shown graphically in Fig. 6-2. The ideal
derivative unit is leading the error by one derivative time
(30 s), while the derivative unit with the filter, after a brief
lag, also leads the error by one derivative time. In practice the
lag does not affect the performance of the algorithm.

Eliminating Proportional Kick on Set Point Changes

Similar to the derivative kick, the sudden change in controller
output caused by the proportional mode right after a change in

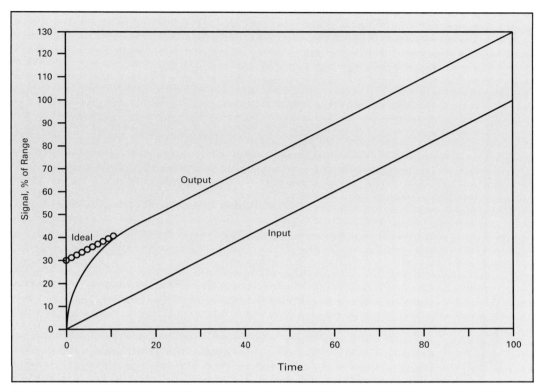

Fig. 6-2. Response of Derivative Unit (P + D) to a Ramp Input with Filter and the Ideal Response without Filter.

set point is known as "proportional kick," although it is not a pulse. It, too, can be eliminated by replacing the error with the appropriate sign of the process variable in the proportional term of Eq. (6-5) and with the output of the derivative unit in Eq. (6-6). Once again modern computer- and microprocessor-based controllers offer the option of having the proportional mode act on the error or on the process variable. However, in this case, the algorithm defaults to proportional on the error unless otherwise specified. The proportional mode must be selected to act on the error when the controller is the slave of a cascade control scheme (see Unit 7).

It is important to realize why the proportional-on-measurement option should be selected for a given controller. The purpose is to allow the operator to make large step changes in set point without fear of causing a sudden change in the controller output. As expected, the resulting approach to the new set point will be slower than if the proportional term acted on the error. The rate of approach to set point is controlled by the reset or integral time when the proportional-on-measurement option is selected.

As in the case of the derivative-on-measurement option, the performance of the controller on disturbance inputs is the same for proportional on error or measurement, because in such cases the set point does not change.

Nonlinear Proportional Gain

Most modern computer- and microprocessor-based controllers offer the option of a nonlinear gain parameter. The purpose is to have the proportional gain increase as the error increases:

$$K_c = K_L (1 + K_{NL} |E_k|) \qquad (6\text{-}7)$$

where K_L is the gain at zero error in %C.O./%T.O., K_{NL} is the increase in gain per unit increase in error, and the bars around the error indicate the absolute value or magnitude of the error, so that the gain increases when the error increases in either the positive or the negative direction. The nonlinear gain is normally used with averaging level controllers (see section 5-2) because it allows a wider variation of the level near the set point while still preventing the tank from overflowing or running dry, as illustrated in Fig. 6-3. The nonlinear gain allows greater smoothing of flow variations with a given tank (that is, makes the tank look bigger than it is) as long as the flow varies near the middle of its range. Some computer algorithms provide the option of having a zero gain at zero error—a feature that is desirable in some pH control schemes.

Example 6-2, Adjusting the Nonlinear Gain: An averaging level controller is proportional-only with a gain of 1%/%, a set point of 50%, and an output bias of 50%. Determine the value of the nonlinear gain required to reduce the gain at zero error to 0.5%/% while still keeping the tank from overflowing or running dry.

To prevent the tank from overflowing or running dry the valve must be fully opened when the level is at 100% of range and closed when the level is at 0%. Since the set point is 50%, either requirement takes place when the magnitude of the error is 50% (+ or −). Since the output bias is 50%, using the upper limit requirement in Eq. (6-7):

$$100\% = 50\% + K_c (100\% - 50\%)$$

$$= 50\% + 0.5[1 + K_{NL} (50\%)] (50\%)$$

$$K_{NL} = [(100 - 50)/(0.5) (50) - 1]/50 = 0.02$$

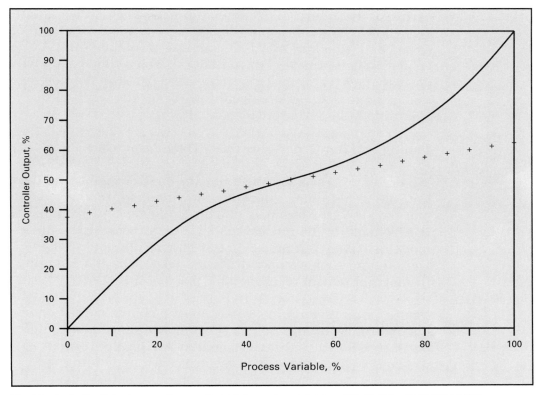

Fig. 6-3. Controller Output versus Process Variable for an Averaging Level Controller with Nonlinear Gain.

or 2% increase in gain per % increase in error. The proportional gain then increases from 0.5 at zero error to 1.0 at 50% error. Recall from Eq. (5-1) that the time constant of the tank is inversely proportional to the controller gain; thus, the effective capacity of the tank for smoothing flow variations can be increased from its real value at full and zero flow to twice that value at half full flow.

6-2. Tuning Computer Feedback Controllers

The tuning formulas of Units 2, 4, and 5, although applicable to continuous controllers, can be applied to digital control algorithms as long as the effect of sampling is taken into consideration. This section presents a simple correction of the tuning formulas for the effect of sampling and formulas that are specifically applicable to digital control algorithms.

Tuning by Ultimate Gain and Period

The formulas for quarter-decay ratio response, which were presented in Unit 2 and are based on the ultimate gain and period of the loop, can be applied directly to computer control algorithms. This is because the test is performed with the loop closed and, thus, the effect of sampling is included in the values of the ultimate gain and period. The ultimate gain will decrease and the ultimate period will increase as the sample time is increased, because sampling makes the feedback control loop less controllable and slower.

Tuning by First-Order plus Dead Time Parameters

When the process parameters of gain, time constant, and dead time are used to tune the controller from the formulas of Unit 4 or the synthesis formulas of Unit 5, the effect of sampling is not included in the process model. This is because the process model is obtained from a step test in controller output (see Unit 3), and such a step will always take place at a sampling instant and remain constant after that.

Moore, et al. (Reference 4), developed a simple correction of the controller tunings for the effect of sampling. They point out that, when a continuous signal is sampled at regular intervals of time and is then reconstructed by holding the sampled values constant for each sampling period, the reconstructed signal is effectively delayed by approximately one half of the sampling interval, as shown in Fig. 6-4. Now, as was shown in Fig. 6-1, the digital-to-analog converter holds the output of the digital controller constant between updates, thus adding one half the sampling time to the dead time of the process components. The correction for sampling is then

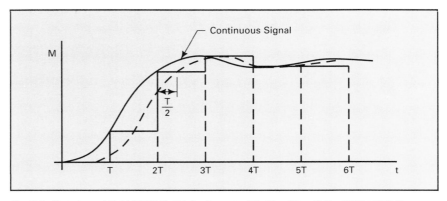

Fig. 6-4. Sample and Hold (DAC) Unit Introduces an Effective Time Delay of One Half the Sample Time.

simply to add one half the sampling time to the dead time obtained from the step response. The uncontrollability parameter is then given by:

$$P_u = \frac{t_0 + 0.5T}{\tau} \tag{6-8}$$

where:

P_u = the uncontrollability parameter
t_0 = the process dead time, min
τ = the process time constant, min
T = the sample interval, min

This equation already appeared in Unit 4 as Eq. (4-2). It was presented there in the hope that this very important correction for the sampling time would not be overlooked in the tuning of digital control algorithms.

Tuning Formulas for Digital Control Algorithms

The procedure of controller synthesis presented in Unit 5, coupled with z-transform analysis, can be used to derive tuning formulas for digital control algorithms. These tuning formulas have the advantage of not being restricted to a correlation range, as are the formulas of Units 2 and 4. The following is a brief outline of the derivation. For the fundamental details see Reference 1.

Consider a process represented by the general second-order plus dead time transfer function:

$$\frac{C(s)}{M(s)} = \frac{Ke^{-t_0 s}}{(\tau_1 s + 1)(\tau_2 s + 1)} \tag{6-9}$$

where K is the process gain in %T.O./%C.O., t_0 is the process dead time in min, and τ_1 and τ_2 are the process time constants in min.

The controller synthesis method of Unit 5 can now be applied to the block diagram of the computer-controlled loop (Fig. 6-1). The block diagram algebra in this case requires use of z transforms and manipulation of pulse transfer functions (see Reference 1).

The Dahlin specification of the closed-loop response for the computer-controlled loop is as follows:

$$C_k = qC_{k-1} + (1 - q)R_{k-N-1} \qquad (6\text{-}10)$$

where:

$q = e^{-T/\tau_c}$
$\tau_c =$ the closed-loop time constant, min
$C =$ the controlled variable
$R =$ the set point
$N =$ the number of complete sample intervals in the dead time

The closed-loop time constant is the same loop performance parameter used in Unit 5. It can be adjusted to shape the tightness of the closed-loop response. Alternatively, parameter q can be used directly. Notice that setting $q = 0$ means that the process variable is specified to match the set point after one dead time, N, plus one sample. Actually, q is the specification of the fraction of the error at any one sample that will remain after one dead time plus one sample. However, for any value of q, the tightness of the closed-loop response depends on the ratio of the sample time to the dominant process time constant, which is why the closed-loop time constant is a better specification of tightness of control.

Using the technique of controller synthesis will obtain a control algorithm that will result in the closed-loop response specified by Eq. (6-10) for the process modeled by Eq. (6-9). Unfortunately, direct use of the resulting algorithm has been shown to cause excessive switching of the controller output, a problem known as "ringing." However, the cause of ringing can be identified and eliminated by slight modification of the algorithm, and the closed-loop time constant specification can be adjusted to compensate for the inaccuracies introduced by the modification. The resulting algorithm can then be written in the following form:

$$\Delta M_k = (1 - q)(M_{k-N-1} - M_{k-1})$$
$$+ \frac{(1 - q)a_1}{1 - a_1}\left[\frac{1}{a_1}Y_k - Y_{k-1}\right] \qquad (6\text{-}11)$$

where:

$$y_k = E_k + \frac{a_2}{1 - a_2}(E_k - E_{k-1})$$
$$a_1 = e^{-T/\tau_1}$$
$$a_2 = e^{-T/\tau_2}$$

The first term on the right-hand side of this formula is a dead time compensation term, which will be discussed in more detail later. Notice that the term is zero if N = 0, that is, if the process dead time is less than one sample time.

The algorithm of Eq. (6-11) can be modified to eliminate the dead time compensation term. When this is done, the resulting formula can be shown to be the series velocity PID algorithm with no filter on the derivative unit. Equation (6-11) can also be rearranged into the parallel form of the velocity PID algorithm. Table 6-1 contains the tuning formulas for both forms of the algorithm. This tuning can be used with the algorithms of Eqs. (6-5) or (6-6), since the effect of the derivative filter on the control algorithm performance is negligible. Recall that the algorithm without the filter can cause undesirable pulses on the controller output for high derivative time-to-sample time ratios.

If only one time constant is available, the second time constant can be set to zero. The resulting algorithm is the velocity PI controller, because the derivative time is then zero.

Notice that, as was the case with the synthesis tuning formulas of Unit 5, the controller gain is tunable, the integral time is a function of the first process time constant, and the derivative time is a function of the second process time constant. The derivative time will always be less than the integral time.

TABLE 6-1. TUNING OF COMPUTER CONTROL ALGORITHMS

$$\text{Let } N = t_0/T \qquad a_1 = e^{-T/\tau_1} \qquad q = e^{-T/\tau_c}$$
$$\text{and} \qquad a_2 = e^{-T/\tau_2}$$

Series PID Algorithm

$$K_c' = \frac{(1 - q)a_1}{K(1 - a_1)[1 + N(1 - q)]}$$

$$T_I' = a_1 T/(1 - a_1) \qquad T_D' = a_2 T/(1 - a_2)$$

Parallel PID Algorithm

$$K_c = \frac{(1 - q)(a_1 - 2a_1 a_2 + a_2)}{K(1 - a_1)(1 - a_2)[1 + N(1 - q)]}$$

$$T_I = \frac{T(a_1 - 2a_1 a_2 + a_2)}{(1 - a_1)(1 - a_2)}$$

$$T_D = \frac{a_1 a_2 T}{a_1 - 2a_1 a_2 + a_2}$$

In the tuning formulas of Table 6-1, setting $q = 0$ results in an upper limit for the controller gain. This value can be used as a guide for the initial tuning of the controller. As was the case with all other tuning formulas, the upper limit of the controller gain decreases with increasing process dead time, parameter N.

The formulas of Table 6-1 can be used for any value of the process parameters and the sample time, and the controller gain can be adjusted to obtain fast response with reasonable variation of the controller output. They are highly recommended because they relate the integral and derivative times to the process time constants, thus reducing the tuning procedure to the adjustment of the controller gain.

Example 6-3, Computer Control of Temperature in Steam Heater: Use the tuning formulas of Table 6-1 to tune the temperature controller for the heater of Fig. 3-1. Use sample times of 1, 2, 4, 8, and 16 s, and the series PID algorithm.

The process parameters for the heater were determined in Example 3-2. They are, using the tangent-and-point method:

$$\text{Gain} = 1\%/\%\qquad \text{Time constant} = 0.62 \text{ min}$$
$$\text{Dead time} = 0.13 \text{ min}$$

As the model has only one time constant, the derivative time resulting from Table 6-1 is zero. That means that the controller becomes a PI controller. The calculation of the tuning parameters is outlined in the following table:

Sample time, s	1	2	4	8	16
Dead time, N	8	4	2	1	0
Maximum gain (q = 0), %/%	4.1	3.6	2.9	2.1	1.8
Integral time, min	0.61	0.60	0.58	0.55	0.49

Notice that the maximum gain is lower and the reset time faster as the sampling interval is increased. This means that the loop is less controllable at the longer sample times. On the other hand, it is not accurate to say that the sampling interval should always be as short as possible. You can observe that the increment in maximum gain is smaller each time the sample time is halved. Recall that for a sample time of 1 s the algorithm must be processed four times more often than for a sample time of four seconds, increasing the work load of the computer or microprocessor and thus reducing the number of loops it can process. There is a point of diminishing returns in selecting the sample time, as will be discussed in detail in the next section.

Fast Process/Slow Sampling

When the sample time is more than three or four times the dominant process time constant, the process reaches steady state in responding to each controller output move before it is sampled again. This may happen because the process is very fast or because the sensor is an analyzer with a long cycle time. For such situations the formulas of Table 6-1 result in a pure integral controller:

$$M_k = M_{k-1} + K_I E_k \qquad (6-12)$$

Tuning: $$K_I = \frac{(1 - q)}{K[1 + N(1 - q)]}$$

Notice that for the case $N = 0$ and $q = 0$, the controller gain is the reciprocal of the process gain. This result makes sense, because a loop gain of 1.0 is needed to reduce the error to zero in one sample if the process reaches steady state during that interval.

Example 6-4, Slow Sampling of Steam Heater Outlet Temperature: For the steam heater of Fig. 3-1, calculate the maximum gain for the PI controller using the formulas of Table 6-1 and sampling times of 32, 64, and 128 seconds. Calculate also the gain of the pure integral controller, given by $K_c T/T_I$.

This problem is a continuation of the progression of the sample time in Example 6-3. The results are summarized in the following table:

Sample time, s	32	64	128	256
Dead time, N	0	0	0	0
Maximum gain (q = 0), %/%	0.73	0.22	0.03	0.001
Integral time, min	0.39	0.23	0.07	0.004
Integral gain, $K_c T/T_I$	1.0	1.0	1.0	1.0

Notice that the integral gain is the same that would result from Eq. (6-12). As the sample time is increased, the proportional term disappears, while the gain of the integral term remains constant.

In summary, the formulas of Table 6-1 are highly recommended for tuning computer control algorithms because they can be used with a first-order plus dead time process model (resulting in a PI algorithm), and with a second-order plus dead time process model (resulting in a PID algorithm). The formulas apply to any combination of values of the process model parameters and sample time.

6-3. Selection of the Algorithm Processing Frequency

Most microprocessor-based controllers have a fixed processing frequency of about two to ten output updates per second. For most feedback control loops, such a short sample time has no effect on controller performance, and the controller can be considered to be continuous. On the other hand, computer control programs allow the control engineer to select the sampling interval of each controller. Unfortunately, some control engineers select the minimum sampling interval for all loops with the mistaken idea that this insures maximum performance of each loop. Although in theory this is true, there is a point of diminishing returns where further reduction in the loop sample time results in minor improvement in loop performance at the expense of overloading the process control computer and limiting the number of loops it can process.

The relationship between sample time and controller performance is a function of the time constant and dead time of the process. In fact, a good way to analyze the selection problem is to look at the ratio of sample time to process time constant versus the ratio of process dead time to time constant or process uncontrollability parameter.

It makes sense to ratio the sample time to the process time constant, because the relative change in the process output from one sample to the next depends only on this ratio; that is, the relative change will be the same for a process with a 1-min time constant sampled once every 5 seconds as for a process with a 10-min time constant sampled every 50 seconds.

It also makes sense to relate the sample time to the uncontrollability parameter, because the dead time imposes a limit on controller performance; this limit is met at higher sample time-to-time constant ratios the higher the dead time-to-time constant ratio is for the process.

Either the loop gain KK_c predicted by any of the tuning formulas or the ultimate loop gain may be used to measure the controller performance, because the higher the loop gain, the smaller the effect of disturbances on the process variable. In Fig. 6-5 the maximum loop gain, calculated using the tuning formula from Table 6-1, is plotted versus the sample time-to-time constant ratio for different dead time-to-time constant ratios. The process is modeled by a first-order plus dead time model, and the calculations are similar to those of Example 6-3.

The graphs of Fig. 6-5 show that, as the sample time-to-time constant ratio is decreased, the maximum loop gain approaches a maximum. The sample time at which this happens depends on the dead time. However, there is not

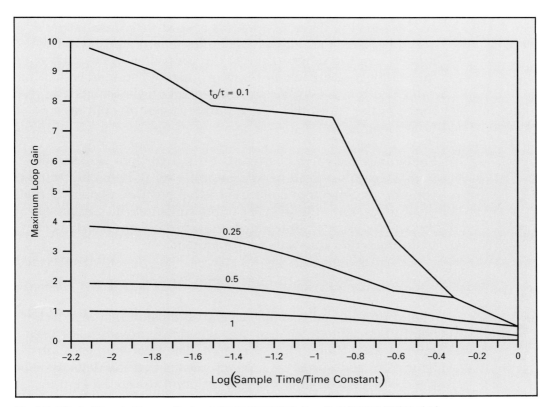

Fig. 6-5. Effect of Sample Time on Maximum Proportional Gain (q = 0) at Various Ratios of t_0/τ.

much increase in the loop gain as the sample time is decreased beyond a value of roughly one tenth the time constant, except for very low dead time-to-time constant ratios. Even for that exception the loop gain is very high at a sample time of one tenth the time constant, so the following rule of thumb for selecting the sample time can be adopted:

$$\text{Sample Time} = \text{(Time Constant)}/10$$

By selecting the proper sample time for each loop, the control engineer can increase the number of loops the process control computer can handle.

Optimizing Feedback Loops

Many modern computer control installations use feedback controllers to minimize the consumption of energy and maximize production rate. A very common example is the technique of "valve position control," in which a controller looks at the output of another controller or valve position and keeps it close to fully opened or fully closed. Such controllers are designed to drive the process toward its constraints over a very long time period; their sample times should be much longer than the sample time of the controller whose output they control—perhaps 30 times or longer. The idea is that the valve position controller should not act on the same time frame as the controller whose output it controls but on a much longer one.

Sometimes the valve position control algorithm is designed with a "gap" or dead band around its set point so that it takes action only when the controlled valve position is outside that dead band. Both the longer sample time and the gap prevent the valve position controller from introducing disturbances and interaction into the control system.

6-4. Feedback Control Algorithm with Dead Time Compensation

The tuning formulas so far have all indicated that feedback controllers cannot perform well when the process has a high ratio of dead time to time constant. The total loop gain must be low for such processes, which means that the deviations of the controlled variable from its set point cannot be kept low in the presence of disturbances. One way to improve the performance of the feedback controller for low controllability loops is to use the computer memory to compensate for the dead time. This section examines two controllers that have been proposed to compensate for dead time: the Smith Predictor and the Dahlin Controller.

The Smith Predictor

Smith (Reference 5) proposed a dead time compensator that consisted of an internal model of the process to be driven on-line by the controller output and continuously compared with the controlled variable to correct for model errors and disturbances. A block diagram of the scheme, known as the ''Smith Predictor,'' is shown in Fig. 6-6. Notice that in the process model the dead time term is separated from the rest of the model transfer function so that the model output, after being corrected for model error and disturbance effects, can be fed to the feedback controller in such a manner that the process dead time is bypassed (hence, the compensation for dead time).

A disadvantage of the Smith Predictor is that, although it requires a model of the process, it does not use it to design or tune the feedback controller, so it ends up with too many adjustable parameters: the model parameters plus the controller tuning parameters. Because there are so many parameters to adjust, there is no convenient way to adjust the closed-loop response when the model does not properly fit the

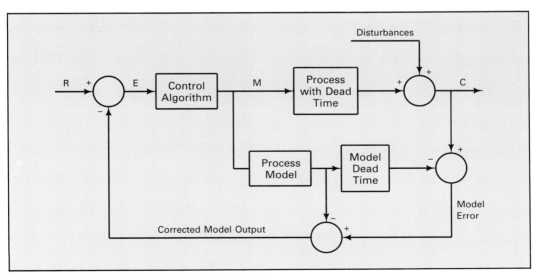

Fig. 6-6. Block Diagram of Smith Predictor.

process. Given the nonlinear nature of process dynamics, any technique that depends heavily on exact process modeling is doomed to fail.

The Dahlin Controller

In section 5-3, in considering a process model with dead time to synthesize the controller for the Dahlin response, Eq. (5-19) was obtained for the controller transfer function. That transfer function contained a time delay term in its denominator, which, if implemented, compensates for the process dead time. It can be shown through block diagram algebra that the Dahlin Controller is exactly equivalent to the Smith Predictor if synthesis is used to design the controller in the predictor scheme.

The dead time in the Dahlin Controller transfer function requires that past values of the controller output be stored and played back. Not until the advent of computer-based controllers was the storage and playback of control signals possible. The computer memory provides the ability to store and retrieve past sampled values. Thus, the algorithm to use is the computer algorithm encountered in section 6-2 as Eq. (6-11). By comparison of Eq. (6-11) with the series velocity algorithm, Eq. (6-4), the algorithm with dead time compensation can be written as follows:

$$\Delta M_k = (1 - q) (M_{k-N-1} - M_{k-1})$$
$$+ K_c'[E_k - E_{k-1} + (T/T_I')E_k] \qquad (6\text{-}13)$$

where:

$$E_k = R_k - Y_k$$

$$Y_k = \frac{\alpha T_D'}{T + \alpha T_D'} Y_{k-1} + \frac{T}{T + \alpha T_D'} C_k$$

$$+ \frac{(\alpha + 1) T_D'}{T + \alpha T_D'} (C_k - C_{k-1})$$

The first term in the calculation of the output provides the dead time compensation. It can also be added to the parallel velocity algorithm of Eq. (6-5). The tuning of the series algorithm is the same as in Table 6-1, except for the controller gain, which is given by:

$$K_c' = \frac{(1 - q)a_1}{K(1 - a_1)} \tag{6-14}$$

Notice that this results in a higher gain than the formula in Table 6-1 because it does not contain the dead time parameter N in the denominator. In fact, the gain produced by Eq. (6-14) is the one that would be obtained from Table 6-1 for a process with no dead time. This is because the dead time compensation term takes care of the dead time.

The Dahlin dead time compensation algorithm is simply a PID algorithm with an extra term added to compensate for dead time. That extra term drops out if the dead time is less than the sample time (N = 0). The algorithm reduces to PI when a first-order plus dead time model is used.

The Dahlin Controller is used extensively to control processes with long dead times. A common application is in the control of paper machines, where the properties of the paper can be measured only after it has gone through the long drying process, which introduces significant dead time.

Example 6-5, Dead Time Compensation Control of Steam Heater: Compare the response of the temperature controller for the steam heater of Fig. 3-1 using the Dahlin Controller with dead time compensation versus a standard PID controller. Assume a velocity PID algorithm with the recommended sample time of 0.05 min (3 s), which is approximately one tenth of the time constant (0.62 min).

The dead time compensation term requires 2 samples of dead time:

$$N = int(t_0/T) = int(0.13/0.05) = int(2.6) = 2$$

The tuning parameters, using the formulas of Table 6-1, are:

$$a_1 = exp(-0.05/0.62) = 0.923 \qquad a_2 = 0$$

Without dead time compensation (q = 0.5):

$$K_c = (1 - 0.5) (0.923/0.077)/(1)[1 + 2(1 - 0.5)] = 3.0\%/\%$$

$$T_I = (0.923/0.077)0.05 = 0.60 \text{ min}$$

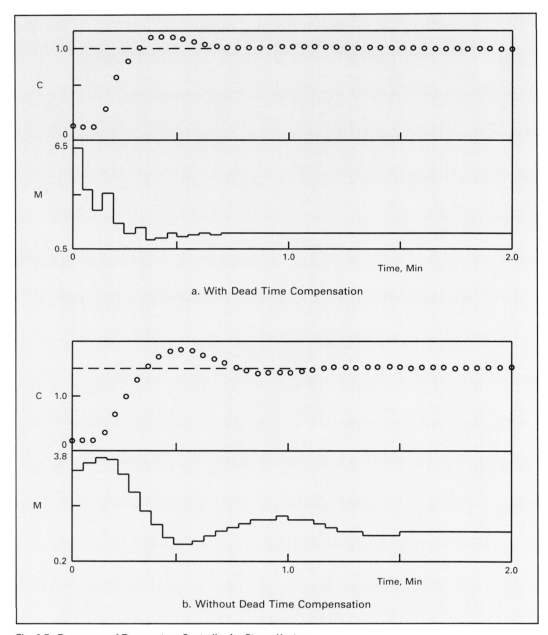

a. With Dead Time Compensation

b. Without Dead Time Compensation

Fig. 6-7. Responses of Temperature Controller for Steam Heater.

With dead time compensation (q = 0.5):

$$K_c = (1 - 0.5) (0.923/0.077)/1 = 6.0\%/\%$$

$$T_I = 0.60 \text{ min}$$

The responses of the controllers are shown in Fig. 6-7. Notice that the dead time compensation controller has a faster rise time with less overshoot (10% vs. 25%) than the regular PI controller at the expense of more variability in the controller output. The value of q = 0.5 was selected to prevent excessive variability in the controller output.

More sophisticated dynamic compensation algorithms have been proposed in the last few years, for example, the Vogel-Edgar Algorithm (Reference 6) and Internal Model Control (Reference 3). These algorithms can incorporate a more precise compensator than the Dahlin algorithm, provided that a precise model of the process is available. Nevertheless, the Dahlin algorithm has been applied successfully to the control of paper machines and other processes with high dead time-to-time constant ratios.

6-5. Summary

This unit has presented various computer feedback controllers, how to tune them, and how to select the sample time for them. The series velocity algorithm, Eq. (6-6), with the tuning formulas of Table 6-1, is strongly recommended and the most commonly used in computer control applications. For processes with high dead time-to-time constant ratios, the Dahlin dead time compensation algorithm, Eq. (6-13), is commonly used in industry and also recommended here.

Exercises

6-1. *What are the two advantages of the velocity PID algorithm over the position algorithm?*

6-2. *What is "derivative kick"? How is it prevented? Why is a "dynamic gain limit" needed in the derivative term of the PID algorithm?*

6-3. *How and why would you eliminate "proportional kick" on set point changes? Will the process variable approach its set point faster or slower when proportional kick is avoided? When must you not avoid proportional kick?*

6-4. *Why is it important to differentiate between series and parallel versions of the PID algorithm? When doesn't it matter?*

6-5. *What is the advantage of the nonlinear proportional gain in averaging level control situations? In such a case, what must the nonlinear gain be for the gain to be 0.25%/% at zero error and still have the controller output reach its limits when the level reaches its limits (0 and 100%)?*

6-6. *A process has a gain of 1.6%T.O./%C.O., a time constant of 10 min, and a dead time of 2.5 min. Calculate the tuning parameters for a PID algorithm if the sample time is (a) 4 s, (b) 1 min, (c) 10 min, and (d) 50 min.*

6-7. *Repeat exercise 6-6, but for a PID algorithm with dead time compensation. Specify also how many samples of dead time compensation, N, must be used in each case.*

6-8. *What is the basic idea behind the Smith Predictor? What is its major disadvantage? How does the Dahlin Controller with dead time compensation overcome the disadvantage of the Smith Predictor?*

References

1. Corripio, A. B., "Digital Control Techniques," *AIChE Modular Instruction Series*, Module A3.8 (New York: AIChE, 1982).
2. Dahlin, E. B., "Designing and Tuning Digital Controllers," *Instruments and Control Systems*, V. 41 (June 1968), p. 77.
3. Garcia, C. E., and Morari, M., "Internal Model Control, 1. A Unifying Review and Some Results," *Industrial and Engineering Chemistry Process Design and Development*, V. 21 (1982), pp. 308–323.
4. Moore, C. F.; Smith, C. L.; and Murrill, P. W., "Simplifying Digital Control Dynamics for Controller Tuning and Hardware Lag Effects," *Instrument Practice*, V. 23 (Jan. 1969), p. 45.
5. Smith, O. J. M., "Closer Control of Loops with Dead Time," *Chemical Engineering Progress*, V. 53 (May 1957), pp. 217–219.
6. Vogel, E. F., and Edgar, T. F., "A New Dead Time Compensator for Digital Control," *Proceedings ISA/80* (Research Triangle Park, NC: ISA, 1980).

Unit 7:
Tuning Cascade Control Systems

UNIT 7

Tuning Cascade Control Systems

Cascade control is a common strategy for improving the performance of process control loops. In its simplest form it consists of closing a feedback loop inside the primary control loop by measuring an intermediate process variable. This unit explains when to apply cascade control and how to tune the controllers in a cascade control system.

Learning Objectives — When you have completed this unit you should:

A. Know when to apply cascade control and why.

B. Be able to select the control modes and tune the controllers in a cascade control system.

C. Recognize reset windup in cascade control systems and know how to prevent it.

7-1. When To Apply Cascade Control

Figure 7-1 shows a typical cascade control system for controlling the temperature in a jacketed exothermic chemical reactor. The control objective is to control the temperature in the reactor. However, instead of having the reactor temperature controller, TIC 1, directly manipulate the jacket coolant valve, the jacket temperature is measured and controlled by a different controller, TIC 2, which manipulates the valve. The output of the reactor temperature controller, TIC 1, or "master" controller, is connected or cascaded to the set point of the jacket temperature controller, TIC 2, or "slave" controller. Notice that only the reactor temperature set point is maintained at the operator set value; the jacket temperature set point varies to whatever value is required to maintain the reactor temperature at its set point. A block diagram of the reactor cascade control strategy, shown in Fig. 7-2, clearly shows that the slave control loop is inside the master control loop.

There are three major advantages to using cascade control:

- Any disturbances that affect the slave variable are detected and compensated by the slave controller before they have

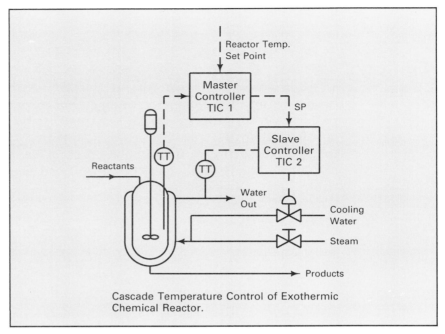

Cascade Temperature Control of Exothermic Chemical Reactor.

Fig. 7-1. Cascade Temperature Control on a Jacketed Exothermic Chemical Reactor.

time to affect the primary control variable. Examples of such disturbances for the reactor of Fig. 7-1 are the coolant inlet temperature and the header pressure.

- The controllability of the outside loop is improved because the inside loop speeds up the response of the process dynamic elements between the control valve and the slave variable. In the reactor example, the speed of response of the jacket is increased, resulting in a more controllable loop for the reactor temperature.

- Nonlinearities of the process in the inner loop are handled by that loop and removed from the more important outer loop. In the reactor example, the nonlinear relationship between temperature and coolant flow is made (by the cascade arrangement) a part of the inner loop, while the outer loop enjoys the linear relationship between reactor and jacket temperatures. As the inner loop should be more controllable than the overall loop, variations in the process gain are less likely to cause instability when isolated in the inner loop.

Because cascade control requires investment in an additional sensor (TT 2) and controller (TIC 2), it is important that these three advantages result in significant improvement in control

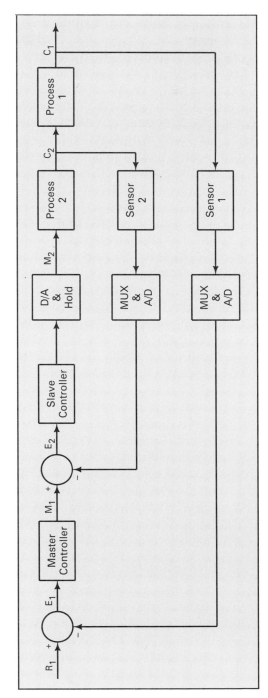

Fig. 7-2. Block Diagram of Cascade Control System.

performance. Such improvement depends on the inner loop responding faster than the outer loop, because all three advantages depend on it. If the inner loop is not faster than the outer loop, disturbances into the inner loop will not be eliminated fast enough to avoid affecting the primary control variable. Speeding up of the inner loop would result in a decrease in the controllability of the overall loop, because its dead time-to-time constant ratio would increase and nonlinearities would become a part of the slower and possibly less controllable loop, thus affecting the stability of the control system.

Along with the inner loop being faster than the outer loop, the success of cascade control also requires that the sensor of the inner loop be fast and reliable. No one would consider, for example, cascading a temperature controller to a chromatographic analyzer controller. On the other hand, the sensor for the inner loop does not have to be accurate—only repeatable—because the integral mode in the master controller will compensate for errors in the measurement of the slave variable. In other words, it is all right for the inner loop sensor to be wrong as long as it is consistently wrong.

Finally, cascade control would not be able to improve the performance of loops that are already very controllable (such as, for example, liquid level and gas pressure control loops) or when it is not required to maintain the controlled variable tightly around its set point (e.g., averaging level control). Although it may be justifiable to cascade a level controller to a flow controller, it would have to be justified by greater flexibility in the operation of the process, not by improved control performance.

7-2. Selection of Controller Modes for Cascade Control Systems

In a cascade control system, the master controller has the same function as the controller in a single feedback control loop: to maintain the primary control variable at its set point. Therefore, the selection of controller modes for the master controller should follow the same guidelines given for a single controller in Unit 5. On the other hand, the function of the slave controller is not the same as that of the master or single controller; it, therefore, requires different design guidelines.

Unlike the master or single feedback controller, the slave controller is constantly having to respond to changes in set point, which it must follow as quickly as possible with a small overshoot and decay ratio. It is also desirable that the slave controller transmit changes in its set point to its output as quickly as possible and, if possible, amplify them. The output of the slave controller is the one that manipulates the final control element, and, if it is to speed up the response of the master controller, it must transmit changes in the master controller output (slave set point) to the final control element at least as fast as if it were not there. It is evident, then, that the slave controller must have proportional mode, and that the proportional mode must act on the error signal and should have a proportional gain of 1.0 or greater if stability permits it.

If the gain of the slave controller is greater than one, changes in the master controller output result in higher immediate changes in the final control element than when a single feedback loop is used. This amplification results in a faster response of the master loop.

Integral Mode in the Slave Controller

The use of integral and derivative modes on the slave controller depends on the application. Recall from previous units that adding integral mode results in a reduction of the proportional gain, while adding derivative mode results in an increase in the proportional gain. This may suggest that all slave controllers should be proportional-derivative (PD) controllers, but such is not the general case.

As mentioned earlier, integral mode is not needed in the slave controller to eliminate the offset, because the integral mode of the master controller can adjust the set point of the slave controller to compensate for the offset. However, if the slave loop is fast and subject to large disturbances (e.g., a flow loop), the offset in the slave controller would require corrective action by the master controller and, therefore, a deviation of the primary controlled variable from its set point. A fast-acting integral mode on the slave controller would eliminate the need for corrective action from the master controller and the deviation in the primary controlled variable.

The integral mode should not be used in those slave loops in which the gain is limited by stability nor those in which the disturbances into the inner loop do not cause large offsets in the secondary controlled variable. The jacket temperature controller of the reactor in Fig. 7-1 is a typical example of a slave loop that does not require integral mode.

Derivative Mode in the Slave Controller

There is an often repeated rule that derivative mode should not be used in both the slave and the master controllers. Since derivative would do the most good on the less controllable loop (which is the outer loop), the rule essentially is reduced to never having derivative mode in the slave controller. There are two reasons for this rule: first, having all three modes in both the master and the slave controllers results in six tuning parameters, which, without the proper guidelines, makes the tuning task more difficult; second, it is undesirable to put two derivative units in series in the loop. Both of these reasons can be argued away as follows:

- Guidelines, such as those given in previous units, simplify the task of tuning. For example, keeping the derivative time about one fourth the integral time reduces the number of parameters in the cascade loop to four: two gains and two integral times.
- By having the derivative of the slave controller act on the process variable instead of on the error, it will not be in series with the derivative unit in the master controller.

The purpose of the derivative unit on the slave controller is to compensate for the sensor lag or loop dead time and allow for a higher slave controller gain with less overshoot and low decay ratio.

When the inner loop is fast and very controllable (as, for example, flow loops), the slave controller does not require derivative mode.

7-3. Tuning the Controllers in a Cascade Control System

The tuning of the controllers in a cascade control system must be carried out from the inside out; that is, the innermost loop must be tuned first, then the loop around it, and so on. This is shown in the block diagram of Fig. 7-2; the inner loop is part of the process for the outer loop.

Each loop in a cascade system must be tuned tighter and faster than the loop around it. Otherwise, the set point of the slave loop would vary more than its measured variable, resulting in poorer control of the master variable. Ideally, the slave variable should follow its set point as quickly as possible, but with little overshoot and oscillations. Quarter-decay ratio response is not recommended for the slave controller because it overshoots set point changes by 50%. The ideal overshoot for the slave variable to a set point change is 5%, which is close to the minimum IAE response for set point changes (see Table 4-5).

After the inner loop is tuned, the master loop can be tuned to follow any desired performance criterion by any of the methods of Units 2, 4, 5, and 6. Given that what makes cascade systems special is the tuning of the slave loop, an examination of some typical slave loops (namely, flow, temperature, and pressure) is in order. Remember, however, that any variable, including composition, can be used as a slave variable, provided it can be measured fast and reliably.

Slave Flow Loop

In modern computer control systems, flow is the innermost loop in most cascade control schemes, because it allows the operator to intervene by taking direct control of the manipulated flow. A typical temperature to flow control scheme is shown in Fig. 7-3. The flow transmitter compensates for variations in the pressure drop across the control valve and absorbs any nonlinearities of the valve. If

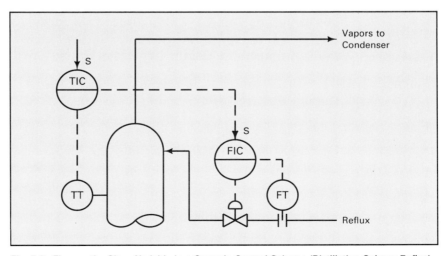

Fig. 7-3. Flow as the Slave Variable in a Cascade Control Scheme (Distillation Column Reflux).

the square root of the differential pressure is extracted, the measured variable of the slave loop and, thus, the output of the master controller become linear with the flow.

The flow controller in a cascade scheme must be tuned tight. A proportional-integral (PI) controller can be used with the integral time set equal to the time constant of the valve actuator (see the synthesis method in Unit 5) and with a gain greater than 1. If hysteresis or deadband in the valve position is a problem, the high gain of the flow controller will reduce the variations in flow required to overcome the hysteresis.

Slave Temperature Loop

Two difficulties with using temperature as the slave measured variable are the sensor lag and the possibility of reset windup, both of which can be handled. The sensor lag can be compensated by using derivative mode in the slave controller, with the derivative time set equal to the sensor time constant. The derivative unit must act on the measured variable only, not on the error, to prevent the connection of two derivative units in series in the loop.

The reactor temperature control scheme of Fig. 7-1 is a typical example of a slave temperature controller. In this application the temperature has the advantage over the coolant flow that it compensates for changes in both coolant header pressure and temperature, while coolant flow will compensate only for variations in coolant header pressure. The temperature controller also closes a loop around the jacket, reducing its effective time constant, thus making the reactor temperature control loop more controllable.

Slave Pressure Loop

Pressure is a good slave variable to use because it can be measured easily, fast, and reliably. A temperature to pressure cascade system is shown in Fig. 7-4. The pressure in the steam chest in the reboiler directly determines the heat transfer rate because it controls the steam condensing temperature and, therefore, the difference in temperature across the heat transfer area. Pressure also has the difficulty of reset windup.

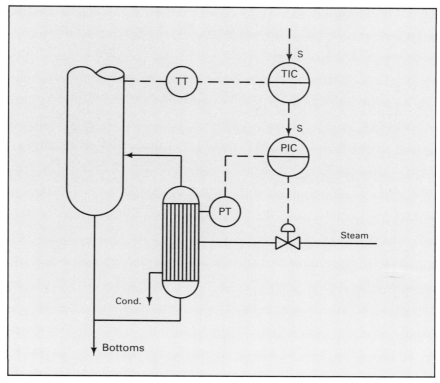

Fig. 7-4. Pressure as the Slave Variable in a Cascade Control Scheme (Distillation Column Reboiler).

Another difficulty with pressure as a slave variable is that it can move out of the transmitter range and thus get out of control. For example, in the scheme of Fig. 7-4, if at low production rate the reboiler temperature drops below 100°C (212°F), the pressure in the steam chest will drop below atmospheric pressure, getting out of the transmitter range, unless the pressure transmitter is calibrated to read negative pressures (vacuum).

Computer Cascade Control

When both the master and the slave controllers are carried out on the computer, the inner loop is usually processed at a higher frequency than the outer loop so that the slave controller has time to respond to a set point change from the master controller before the next change takes place. Recall that the inner loop should respond faster than the outer loop.

One important consideration when digital feedback algorithms are cascaded is bumpless transfer from manual to automatic. This is accomplished by initializing the output of the master controller to the measured (process) variable of the slave controller when the loops are switched to automatic control, making for a smooth transition to automatic in most cases.

The following is an example of a very successful industrial application of cascade control. It is an example of composition to composition cascade, which is not very common. It also shows a three-level cascade control system, with the flow controller being the lowest level.

Example 7-1, Control of Hydrogen/Nitrogen Ratio in an Ammonia Synthesis Loop: A simplified diagram of the synthetic ammonia process is shown in Fig. 7-5. Air, natural gas (CH_4) and steam are mixed in the reforming furnace and, after the carbon dioxide (CO_2) is removed, a mixture of

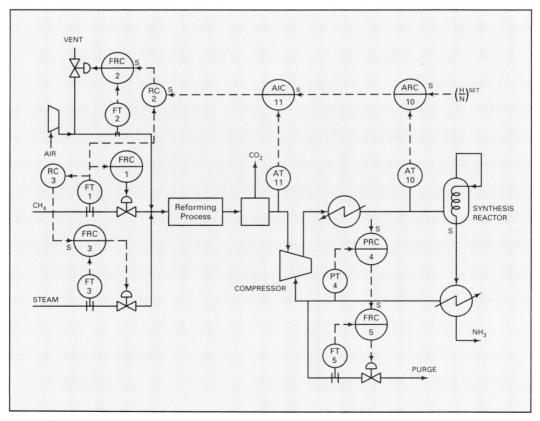

Fig. 7-5. **Cascade Control of Reactor Inlet Composition and Pressure in the Ammonia Synthesis Loop.**

hydrogen and nitrogen is obtained and fed to the synthesis loop compressor. The flow in the synthesis loop is about six to seven times the flow of fresh feed, as the synthesis reactor converts only about 15% of the H_2 and N_2 mixture to ammonia (NH_3) in each pass. This high recycle-to-fresh feed ratio makes for a long time constant for the synthesis loop in comparison to the short time constant for the reforming process—a situation ideal for cascade control.

The objective is to control the H/N ratio of the mixture into the synthesis reactor at its optimum value (about 2.85 for a slight excess of nitrogen). The master controller (ARC 10) receives the measurement of the composition at the reactor inlet from a very accurate analyzer (AT 10). The output of the master controller adjusts the set point on the slave controller (AIC 11). The slave controller receives the measurement of the composition of the fresh feed from a fast and inexpensive analyzer (AT 11, usually a simple thermal conductivity detector), and its output adjusts the ratio of air to natural gas. The ratio controller, in turn, adjusts the set point of the process air flow controller (FRC 2).

This example illustrates the point made earlier that the slave measurement need not be accurate but must be fast. Errors in the slave measurement are corrected by the integral mode of the master controller. On the other hand, the measurement of the master controller can be slow, but it must be accurate. Disturbances in the reforming process are handled quickly by the slave controller before they have a chance to affect the primary controlled variable.

Figure 7-5 also shows a pressure to flow cascade loop for the control of the pressure in the synthesis loop. In this cascade the master controller is the pressure controller (PRC 4), and the slave controller is the purge flow controller (FRC 5). The purge is a small stream removed from the loop to eliminate the accumulation of inert gases (argon and methane) and the excess nitrogen.

Although both cascade control loops of Fig. 7-5 could be carried out with analog controllers, computer control offers an unexpected virtue to this scheme: patience. For example, in one installation where the pressure control scheme was carried out with analog controllers, the master controller was operated on manual because it was swinging the purge flow all over its range. This was because the process for this loop has a time constant of about one hour. A digital controller with a sample time of 5 minutes and an integral time of 45 minutes was able to maintain the pressure at its optimum set point on the same installation.

7-4. Reset Windup in Cascade Control Systems

Unit 5 explained that a discrepancy between the operating ranges of the single feedback controller output and the control valve causes undesirable overshoot of the controlled variable during recovery from a period of saturation of the control valve. Such range discrepancies are more common in cascade control systems because the range of the transmitter on the slave loop is usually wider than the operating range of the variable, particularly when the slave variable is temperature or pressure.

To illustrate the problem of cascade windup, consider the start-up of the jacketed reactor of Fig. 7-1. Initially, both controllers are on manual, with the cooling water valve closed and the steam valve manually opened to bring the reactor up to the operating temperature, say 55°C. The jacket temperature transmitter, TT 2, has a range of 0 to 120°C, and the steam condenses at 110°C, which is the value of the jacket temperature when the steam valve is closed and the cascade control system is initialized and switched to automatic. To prevent overheating, this is done before the reactor temperature reaches its set point—say when it reaches 50°C.

Following the bumpless transfer procedure of the control program, the output of the master controller is initialized to the measured temperature of the slave controller, 110°C. At this time, the jacket temperature begins to drop because the steam has been turned off and the reactor is at the lower temperature of 50°C.

Meanwhile, the reactor temperature slowly increases because of the heat of the reaction. For the time that the reactor temperature is between 50 and 55°C (its set point), the control situation is as follows:

• The slave controller sees a jacket temperature below its set point (110°C) and calls for the cooling water valve to remain closed.

- The master controller also sees its temperature below set point and calls for an increase in the jacket temperature set point above the current 110°C value.

Most computer control programs will detect that the slave controller output is limited or "clamped" at the closed position and will prevent the master controller from increasing its output, as this would only call for closing of the coolant valve, which is already closed. Does this logic prevent the cascade control system from winding up? What happens next?

Notice that a gap has been created between the set point of the slave controller, frozen at 110°C, and its measured temperature. As the reactor temperature crosses its set point of 55°C, the master controller starts decreasing the set point of the slave controller to bring the temperature down. However, the coolant valve will not open until the set point of the slave controller drops below its measured temperature, that is, until the gap mentioned earlier is overcome. As the set point of the slave controller will change at a rate controlled by the integral time of the master controller, it takes a long time for the coolant valve to open and the reactor temperature overshoots its set point badly—the common symptom of reset windup. By the time the coolant valve starts to open, the reactor temperature has reached its trip point of 60°C, and the entire system is shut down by dumping the reactor contents into a pool of water below. Obviously, the saturation or "clamp limit" detection system could not avoid reset windup in this case.

One solution to this problem is to re-initialize the output of the master controller to the measured value of the jacket temperature as long as the slave controller output is clamped. This way, the gap that causes the windup is eliminated, and the coolant valve opens the moment the reactor temperature crosses its set point; at that point, the master controller will call for a lower jacket temperature than its current value, and the slave controller will respond by opening the coolant value.

A more elegant cascade windup protection method, one that does not require any logic, is the use of a "reset feedback" signal on the control algorithm. In the cascade scheme the reset feedback signal is the measured variable of the slave loop, expressed in percent of transmitter range. It is used in the calculation of the controller output by the velocity algorithm as follows:

$$M_k = b_k + \Delta M_k \qquad (7\text{-}1)$$

where:

M_k = the output of the master controller and set point of the slave controller

b_k = the reset feedback variable (in this case, the measured variable of the slave loop

ΔM_k = the incremental output of the master controller, which is calculated by the velocity algorithm

By using this formula to update the set point of the slave controller at every processing of the master controller, there is no possibility of windup; the master controller will call for an increase or decrease of the slave variable from its current value, not from the previous set point. The use of the reset feedback approach requires that the slave loop be processed more frequently than the master loop and that the slave controller have integral mode. Otherwise, any offset in the slave controller would cause an offset in the master controller, even if the master controller had integral mode.

A third approach to protect against cascade windup is to set clamp limits on the set point of the slave controller that correspond to its actual operating limits. For the jacketed reactor example, these limits would be the coolant inlet temperature and the reactor set point. However, notice that these limits change during normal operation, and it would be tedious to have to constantly change them to match operating conditions.

7-5. Summary

This unit explored the reasons for cascade control, the selection of modes for the slave controller, and the procedure for tuning cascade control systems, as well as cascade windup and ways to protect against it. Cascade control has proliferated in computer control installations because there is essentially no cost for the additional slave controllers. The only additional cost in a computer control system is the cost of one transmitter and one multiplexer input channel for each slave loop.

Exercises

7-1. What are the three major advantages of cascade control?

7-2. What is the main requirement for a cascade control system to result in improved control performance? What is required of the sensor for the slave loop?

7-3. Are the tuning and selection of modes different for the master controller in a cascade control system from those for the controller in a simple feedback control loop? Explain.

7-4. What is different about the slave controller in a cascade control system? When should it not have integral mode? If the slave is to have derivative mode, should it operate on the process variable or the error?

7-5. In what order must the controllers in a cascade control system be tuned? Why?

7-6. What are the two major difficulties with using temperature as the process variable of the slave controller in a cascade control system? How can they be handled?

7-7. Why is pressure a good variable to use as the slave variable in cascade control? What are the two major difficulties with using pressure as the slave variable?

7-8. What is the relationship between the processing frequencies of the master and the slave controllers in a computer cascade control system?

7-9. How can reset windup occur in a cascade control system? How can it be avoided?

Unit 8:
Feedforward and Ratio Control

UNIT 8

Feedforward and Ratio Control

This unit considers the advanced strategies of feedforward and ratio control. Along with cascade control, these strategies can be classified as multiple-input single-output (MISO): they require more than one process measurement but only one final control element (valve) since there is only one control objective. Feedforward control consists of measuring and compensating for process disturbances, and ratio is the simplest form of feedforward control in which both the measured disturbance and the manipulated variables are flows.

Learning Objectives — When you have completed this unit you should:

A. Understand when to apply feedforward and ratio control.

B. Know when to use and how to tune a static feedforward compensator.

C. Be able to tune dynamic feedforward compensators.

8-1. Why Feedforward Control?

In Unit 4 it was explained that some feedback loops are more controllable than others and that the parameter that measures the uncontrollability of a feedback loop is the ratio of the dead time to the time constant of the process in the loop. When this ratio is high, of the order of one or greater, feedback control cannot prevent disturbances from causing large deviations of the controlled variable from its set point. It is then that the strategies of feedforward and ratio control can most improve control performance.

The strategy of feedforward control consists of measuring the major disturbances to a control objective and calculating the change in manipulated variable required to compensate for them. The following are characteristics of feedforward control:

- It is theoretically possible to have perfect control, that is, zero error at all times (this is not so for feedback control that must operate on an error).

- An accurate model of the process is needed to design the feedforward controller. The model must include the effects of both the disturbances and the manipulated variable on the controlled variable.
- All disturbances must be measured and compensated. Alternately, feedback trim can be added to compensate for disturbances that have minor effect on the controlled variable or that vary too slowly to merit measurement (e.g., ambient conditions, exchanger scaling).

Feedforward compensation can be a simple proportionality between two signals or complex material and energy balance calculations involving the measured disturbances and the manipulated variable. No matter how simple or complex the steady-state compensation, compensation for process dynamics is usually accomplished with a simple linear lead-lag unit.

The motivation for feedforward control is best presented by comparing it to feedback control. A block diagram of the typical feedback control loop is shown in Fig. 8-1. The following are the characteristics of feedback control that make it so convenient:

1. The controller or PID control algorithm are standard off-the-shelf items.
2. It can be tuned on line by trial and error so a detailed

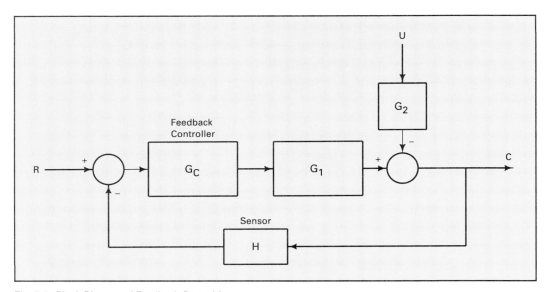

Fig. 8-1. Block Diagram of Feedback Control Loop.

model of the process is not needed to implement feedback control.

3. The integral mode of the controller will compute the value of its output, M, required to keep the controlled variable, C, at its set point, R.

Opposite these very desirable characteristics are two undesirable ones:

1. When a disturbance, U, enters the system, the controlled variable must deviate from its set point before the controller can take action.
2. Overcorrections occur because of delays in the process and the sensor that can cause the controlled variable to oscillate around its set point.

These problems are significant in process systems because of the long time delays involved, sometimes of the order of hours. The remedy to these problems is feedforward control.

Pure Feedforward Control

The block diagram for pure feedforward control is shown in Fig. 8-2. The technique consists of measuring the disturbance U instead of the controlled variable. Corrective action begins as soon as the disturbance enters the system and, in theory, can prevent any deviation of the controlled variable from its set point. However, this requires an exact model of the process and its dynamics, plus exact compensation for all possible

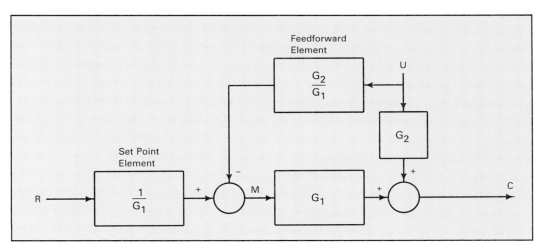

Fig. 8-2. Block Diagram for Pure Feedforward Control.

disturbances. The "set point element" provides a calibrated means to adjust the set point and seldom includes any dynamic compensation.

The "feedforward element" simulates the effect of the disturbance on the controlled variable (block G_2) and compensates for the lags and delays on the manipulated variable (block G_1). Notice that the signals always travel forward (that is, there is no loop in the diagram), so the feedforward controller cannot introduce instability in the process response.

Feedforward-Feedback Control

It is seldom practical to measure all the disturbances that affect the controlled variable. A more reasonable approach is to measure only those disturbances that are expected to cause the greatest deviations in the controlled variable and handle the so-called "minor disturbances" by adding "feedback trim" to the feedforward controller. The block diagram for a feedforward-feedback control system is shown in Fig. 8-3. Notice that the feedback controller takes the place of the set point element of Fig. 8-2, and only the feedforward element is necessary in the combined control scheme. A feedforward element is required for each disturbance measured.

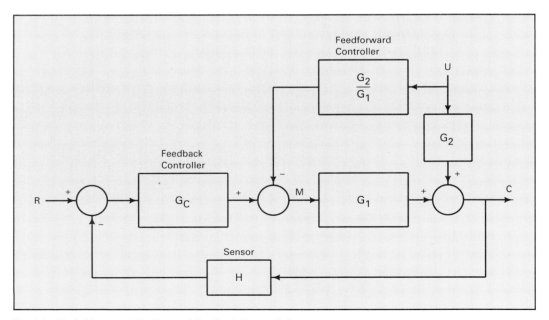

Fig. 8-3. Block Diagram of Feedforward-Feedback Control Scheme.

Notice that, when the outputs of the feedforward and feedback controllers are summed, as in Fig. 8-3, the presence of the feedforward controller does not affect the response of the loop to inputs other than the measured disturbance. In fact, the feedback controller tuning does not have to be adjusted because of the installation of the feedforward controller.

Economics dictate that only those disturbances that are frequent enough and important enough—for their effect on product quality, safety, or similar considerations—should be measured and compensated for with a feedforward controller.

The following are advantages of the feedforward-feedback scheme:

1. The feedback controller takes care of those disturbances that are not important enough to be measured and compensated for.
2. The feedforward controller does not have to compensate exactly for the measured disturbances since any minor errors in the model will be trimmed off by the feedback loop, hence the term, "feedback trim."

Because of these advantages, feedback trim is a part of almost every feedforward control scheme.

Ratio Control

The simplest form of feedforward control is ratio control. It consists simply of the establishment of a ratio between two flows. An example of ratio control between the steam and process flows of a steam heater is shown in Fig. 8-4. In this example the process flow is the disturbance or "wild" flow, and the steam is the manipulated flow. The steam flow controller takes care of variations in the pressure drop across the control valve and its nonlinearity. By maintaining a constant ratio when the process flow is changed by the operator or another controller, the outlet process temperature is kept constant as long as the steam latent heat and process inlet temperature remain constant.

Some control engineers prefer to calculate the ratio by dividing the manipulated flow by the wild flow and then controlling the ratio with a feedback controller, as shown in Fig. 8-5. This alternative has the advantage of displaying the

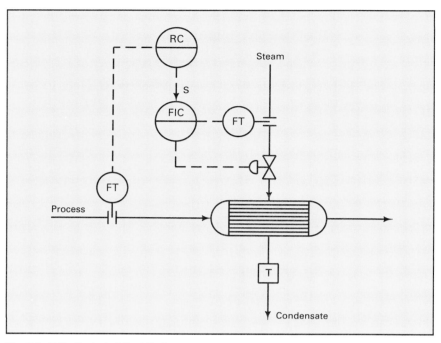

Fig. 8-4. Ratio Control of Heat Exchanger.

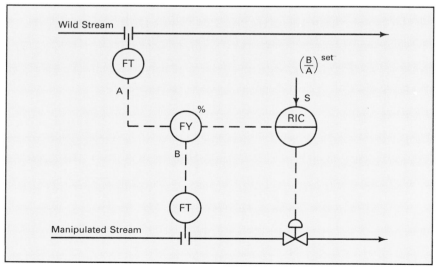

Fig. 8-5. Ratio Control by Feedback Control of the Calculated Ratio.

ratio directly, but at the expense of creating a very nonlinear feedback control loop; notice that the gain of the feedback loop in Fig. 8-5 is inversely proportional to the wild flow, which is the major disturbance. The ratio controllers in some computer control programs display the calculated ratio but do not use it for control. Instead, the output is calculated by multiplying the input or wild flow by the ratio set point, as in Fig. 8-4.

8-2. Design of Linear Feedforward Controllers

Based on the block diagram in Fig. 8-2, the feedforward controller and the process constitute two parallel paths between the disturbance U and the controlled variable C. The controlled variable response is the sum of its responses to the manipulated variable and to the disturbance:

$$C = G_1 M + G_2 U \qquad (8\text{-}1)$$

where M is the manipulated variable and G_1 and G_2 are the transfer functions of the controlled variable to the manipulated variable and the disturbance, respectively.

The value of M required to keep C equal to the set point R is given by

$$M = \frac{1}{G_1} R - \frac{G_2}{G_1} U \qquad (8\text{-}2)$$

This is, therefore, the design equation for the feedforward controller, having the set point R and disturbance U as inputs and the manipulated variable M as output. Equation (8-2) provides the design formulas for both the set point and feedforward elements of Fig. 8-2:

Set point element: $G_s = 1/G_1$ (8-3)

Feedforward element: $G_F = -(G_2/G_1)$ (8-4)

When feedback trim is used, as in Fig. 8-3, only the feedforward element is needed, as the feedback controller takes the place of the set point element.

Simple Linear Models for Feedforward Control

If the process transfer functions G_1 and G_2 are approximated with simple first-order plus dead time models, the feedforward controller can be built out of standard algorithms available in most commercial process control programs. The simplest approximations are first-order plus dead time models (see Unit 3):

$$G_1 = \frac{K_1 e^{-t_{01}s}}{\tau_1 s + 1} \tag{8-5}$$

$$G_2 = \frac{K_2 e^{-t_{02}s}}{\tau_2 s + 1} \tag{8-6}$$

where:

K_1 and K_2 = the process gains, %/%
τ_1 and τ_2 = the time constants, min
t_{01} and t_{02} = the dead times, min

The design formula for the feedforward controller is then obtained by substituting Eqs. (8-5) and (8-6) into Eq. (8-4):

$$G_F = -\frac{K_2}{K_1} \frac{\tau_1 s + 1}{\tau_2 s + 1} e^{-(t_{02} - t_{01})s} \tag{8-7}$$

The linear feedforward controller thus consists of three terms: a steady-state gain, a lead-lag compensator, and a dead time compensator.

Although Eq. (8-7) was derived from simple first-order models, there is no incentive to use dynamic compensation terms of higher order than the simple lead-lag unit. For example, use of second-order models would call for a compensator with two more parameters than the lead-lag unit, making it harder to tune while offering little improvement in performance over a well-tuned lead-lag unit.

The dead time compensator of Eq. (8-7) can be realized only when the dead time between the disturbance and the controlled variable is longer than the dead time between the manipulated variable and the controlled variable. Otherwise, it would call for the feedforward correction to start before the disturbance takes place, which obviously is not possible. The dead time compensator requires the memory of digital devices (computers and microprocessors) for its implementation. Often the dead time compensator can be left out because the lead-lag unit can be tuned to provide all of the required dynamic compensation, thus simplifying the tuning task. In general, the dead time compensator should be used only when the lead-lag unit cannot do the job by itself.

8-3. Tuning of Linear Feedforward Controller

Of the three terms of the design formula, Eq. (8-7), the gain is always required and the dynamic compensators are optional. When only the gain is used, the feedforward controller is called a "static" compensator.

Gain Adjustment

The adjustment of the feedforward gain can be carried out with the feedback controller on manual or automatic. If done with the feedback controller on manual, when the gain is not correct the controlled variable will deviate from its set point after a sustained disturbance input. The gain can then be adjusted until the controlled variable is at the set point again. Because of process nonlinearities, the required feedforward gain may change with operating conditions, so that compensation may not be possible with a simple linear controller.

If the feedforward gain is adjusted with the feedback controller on automatic, the variable to observe is the output of the feedback controller. If the feedback controller has integral mode, the controlled variable will always return to its set point after a disturbance. However, if the feedforward gain is incorrect, the output of the feedback controller will be changed to compensate for the error in the feedforward controller. The feedforward gain must then be adjusted until the feedback controller output returns to its initial value. As before, process nonlinearities will prevent a single value of the gain to work at all process conditions.

The one thing to remember when tuning the feedforward gain is to wait for the system to reach steady state before making the next adjustment.

Tuning the Lead-Lag Unit

The most commonly used feedforward dynamic compensator is the lead-lag unit, which is available both as an analog off-the-shelf device or as a control algorithm in computer control programs. To understand how to tune a lead-lag unit, it is important to know how it responds to step and ramp signals and to realize that both the lead and the lag time constants are adjustable and either can be longer than the other.

The response of the lead-lag unit to a step input is shown in Fig. 8-6 for both the lead being longer than the lag and the lag being longer than the lead, assuming in each case that the gain is unity. Notice that the initial change in the output of the lead-lag unit is always equal to the ratio of the lead to the lag so that there is an initial overcorrection when the lead is longer than the lag and a partial correction when the lag is longer than the lead. In either case, the output approaches the

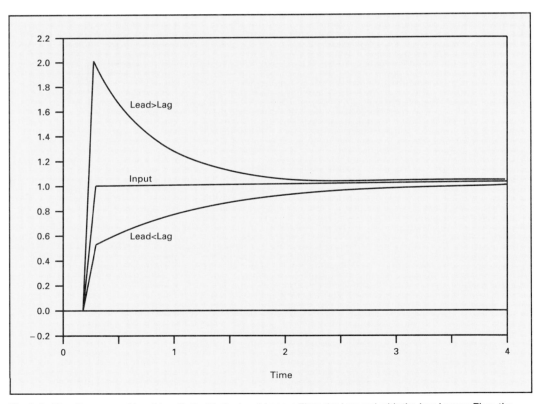

Fig. 8-6. **Step Response of Lead-Lag Unit with the Lead Longer Than the Lag and with the Lag Longer Than the Lead.**

steady-state correction exponentially, at a rate determined by the lag time constant.

Figure 8-7 shows the response of the lead-lag unit to a ramp input, both for the lead longer than the lag and the lag longer than the lead and for unity gain. The figure shows where the names "lead" and "lag" come from: the output of the lead-lag unit, after a transient period, either leads the input ramp by the difference between the lead and the lag or lags it by the difference between the lag and the lead. The ramp response is more typical than the step response to the type of inputs provided by the disturbances in a real process. The ramp can also approximate the rising and dropping portions of slow sinusoidal disturbances.

With the responses to step and ramp inputs in mind, tuning of the lead-lag unit becomes a simple procedure. The only decision is how much to lead or lag the feedforward correction

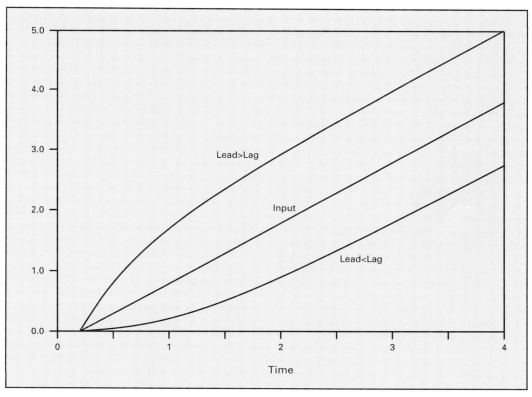

Fig. 8-7. Response of a Lead-Lag Unit to a Ramp with the Lead Longer Than the Lag and with the Lag Longer Than the Lead.

to the disturbance; this fixes the difference between the lead and the lag. Then the ratio of the lead to the lag is selected based on how much to amplify or attenuate sudden changes in the disturbance inputs. For example, suppose it is desired to lead the disturbance by one minute; a lead of 1.1 minutes and a lag of 0.1 minute may be chosen, which gives an amplification factor of 1.1/0.1 = 11, or a lead of 3 minutes and a lag of 2 minutes for an amplification factor of 3/2 = 1.5. If the disturbance is noisy (e.g., a flow), the second choice is preferable since it would result in less amplification of the noise.

Although it is possible to have a lag with zero lead, it is not allowed to have a lead without a lag. The ratio of the lead to the lag should not be greater than 10. When a net lag is required, the lead can usually be set to zero, simplifying the tuning task.

Computer Lead-Lag Algorithm

The exact form of the lead-lag algorithm can be derived from the transfer function of an analog lead-lag unit. It is as follows:

$$Y_k = Y_{k-1} + (1 - a)(KX_k - Y_{k-1}) + K \frac{\tau_{LD}}{\tau_{LG}} (X_k - X_{k-1}) \quad (8\text{-}8)$$

where:

$$X_k = \text{the input at the kth sample}$$
$$Y_k = \text{the output at the kth sample}$$
$$K = \text{the gain of the lead-lag unit, \%/\%}$$
$$\tau_{LD} \text{ and } \tau_{LG} = \text{respectively, the lead and the lag, min}$$
$$a = e^{-T/\tau_{LG}}, \text{ also approximated by } a = \tau_{LG}/(T + \tau_{LG})$$
$$T = \text{the sample time, min}$$

The actual algorithms used in commercial computer control programs use various forms of approximations for the filter parameter a, but it is always a function of the sample time and the lag time constant. Notice that the effect of the lead is to multiply the change in input at each sample by the ratio of the lead to the lag. In other words, for the computer lead-lag algorithm, the input change at each sample is a step change.

Tuning the Dead Time Compensation Term

Besides lead-lag dynamic compensation, the ability of the computer to store information in its memory permits one to compensate for dead time. Dead time compensation should be used only when the dead time is much longer than the time lag that would be used in the lead-lag unit.

Dead time compensation is accomplished by storing the feedforward corrective action at each control update in a memory stack and then retrieving it several sample times later for output to the process. The output of the dead time compensator is equal to its input N samples earlier:

$$Y_k = KX_{k-N} \tag{8-9}$$

where N is the number of samples of dead time and K is the gain. A plot of the responses of dead time compensation to a step and to a ramp are shown in Fig. 8-8. The dead time compensator does not start responding until the dead time and then reproduces the input exactly. It should be used only when a lag without lead would cause the feedforward correction to take place too soon.

The dead time compensator is easy to tune as it has only one dynamic parameter: the number of samples of delay.

Before applying dead time compensation, one must make sure that the dead time does not delay the action in a feedback control loop. Recall that dead time always makes a feedback control loop less controllable. The reason it can be used in feedforward control is that the corrective action always goes forward (that is, no loop is involved).

8-4. Nonlinear Feedforward Compensation

Although linear feedforward compensation can significantly improve control performance, process nonlinearities cause their performance to deteriorate when process conditions change. Simple nonlinear models, based on knowledge of the process, can be used to design feedforward compensators that perform well over a wide range of operating conditions. The idea is to use the basic principles of physics to replace the steady-state gain of the linear feedforward controller with more precise calculations that reflect the full nonlinear

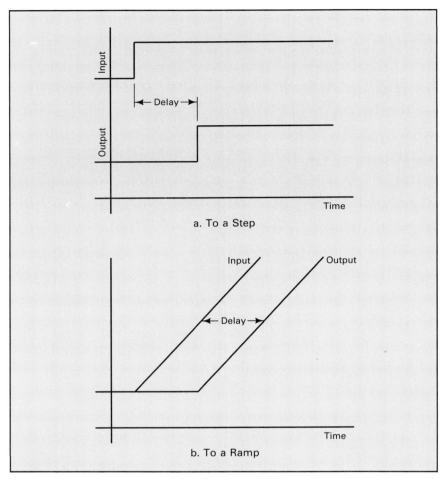

Fig. 8-8. Response of Dead Time Compensator.

interaction between the process variables. To keep the controller simple, it is designed from steady-state relationships; then, lead-lag and dead time compensators are used to compensate for process dynamics.

The outline of the design procedure is as follows:

1. State the control objective, that is, define which variable needs to be controlled and what its set point is. It is useful to write the objective in the form:

$$\text{variable} = \text{set point}$$

The set point should be adjustable by the operator, not a constant.

2. Enumerate the possible measured disturbances. Which disturbances can be easily measured? How much and how fast should each be expected to vary? How much would it cost to measure each of them? It is not really necessary to make a precise cost estimate or get a price bid from a vendor. It is enough to be aware that, for example, a composition sensor may be more expensive to buy and maintain than a flow or temperature sensor.

3. State which variable is going to be manipulated by the feedforward controller. When the feedforward controller is cascaded to a slave controller, the manipulated variable should be defined as the set point of the slave controller (for example, the flow of the manipulated stream instead of the valve position).

4. From basic principles (e.g., material and energy balances), write the formulas that relate all the variables defined in the preceding steps. Keep them as simple as possible. Solve for the manipulated variable so it can be calculated from the measured disturbances and the control objective. The resulting formula or formulas constitute the design equation(s) to be programmed into the computer for on-line execution. Caution: The formula must use the set point of the controlled variable and not its measured value.

5. Reevaluate the list of measured disturbances. The effect of the expected variation of each disturbance on the controlled variable can be calculated from the basic formulas; if it is small, the disturbance need not be measured. On the other hand, a disturbance that was not on the original list may be found from the formulas to have a significant effect on the controlled variable. The decision to measure or not to measure must weigh the effect of the disturbance, its expected magnitude, the speed and frequency of variation, and the cost of measuring it. Unmeasured disturbances are treated as constants in the design equation, equal to their design or average expected values. Alternatively, if difficult to measure but still expected to vary, they may be adjusted by feedback trim.

6. Introduce the feedback trim, if any, into the design equation. This is done by grouping unknown terms and unmeasured disturbances as much as possible and letting the output of the feedback controller adjust the group of terms that is expected to vary most. For example, the heat loss rate from a furnace can be grouped with other unknown terms by incorporating it into a furnace efficiency.

7. Decide whether dynamic compensation is needed and how it is to be introduced into the design. Simple lead-lag or dead time compensators are commonly used. A separate dynamic compensator should be installed on each measured disturbance, but sometimes only one compensator on the output of the feedforward controller can compensate for all the measured disturbances. It is not good practice to install the dynamic compensator in such a way that it becomes part of the feedback trim loop, especially if it contains dead time compensation.

8. Draw the instrumentation diagram for the feedforward controller. This is a diagram showing the various computations and relationships between the signals. It is good practice to draw it so that all the input signals enter from the top (or left), and the output signals exit at the bottom (or right). It is at this point that implementation details, largely dependent on the equipment used, must be decided upon. A good design should be able to continue to operate safely when some of its input measurements fail—a characteristic of the design known as "graceful degradation".

The feedforward controller can then be programmed on the control computer or configured on the distributed control system. The following example illustrates this design procedure. For other good examples, see References 1 and 3.

Example 8-1, Feedforward Temperature Control of a Steam Heater: An example of a nonlinear model for feedforward control is given by the heat exchanger application described in Reference 2. A sketch of the steam heater and feedforward controller is given in Fig. 8-9. The design procedure is as follows:

1. Control objective: $$T_o = T_o^{set} \qquad (8\text{-}10)$$

2. Measured disturbances:

   W—the flow through the exchanger, lb/h
   T_i—the inlet temperature, °F

3. Manipulated variable:

   F—steam flow controller set point, lb/h

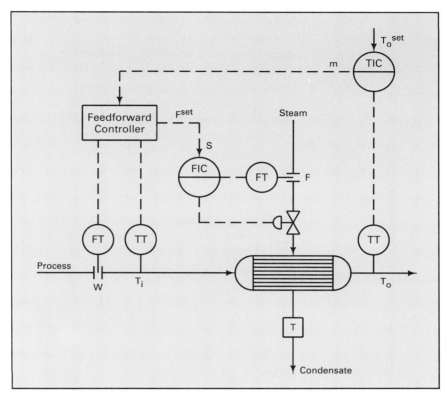

Fig. 8-9. Feedforward Control of Steam Heater.

4. A steady-state energy balance on the exchanger yields the equation for the static feedforward controller:

$$FH_v = WC(T_o - T_i) + Q_L \qquad (8\text{-}11)$$

where:

C = the specific heat of fluid, Btu/lb°F
H_v = the heat of vaporization of the steam, Btu/lb
Q_L = the heat loss rate, Btu/h

5. At this point the effect of the possible disturbances on the outlet temperature would be evaluated, and it might be found that the heat loss rate is as important as the two measured disturbances but difficult to measure, making it a candidate for feedback trim adjustment. Conversely, the inlet temperature might not have enough effect to merit the cost of measuring it, in which case the feedforward

controller becomes a simple steam-to-process flow ratio controller, as in Fig. 8-4.

6. The need for feedback trim is determined by considering how much the unknown terms in the design formula are expected to vary. Here again, the cost of the feedback sensor must be considered. The three unknown terms are the physical properties, C and H_v, and the heat loss rate, Q_L. The three can be lumped by assuming that the heat loss rate is proportional to the heat transfer rate:

$$Q_L = (1 - \text{Eff})FH_v \qquad (8\text{-}12)$$

where Eff is a heater efficiency or fraction of the energy input that is transferred to the process fluid. Substitution of Eq. (8-12) into Eq. (8-11) and solving for the manipulated variable gives the design formula:

$$F^{set} = \frac{C}{H_v\text{Eff}} (T_o^{set} - T_i)W \qquad (8\text{-}13)$$

Notice that the outlet temperature in the formula has been replaced by its set point; that is, the control objective, Eq. (8-10), has been substituted into the design formula to assure that it is enforced by the feedforward controller. In modern computer control systems it is possible to retrieve the set point from the feedback controller to use in the feedforward calculation so that only one set point has to be entered by the operator—a hard design requirement.

All of the unknowns have now been lumped into a single coefficient, $C/H_v\text{Eff}$; it would seem natural for the feedback trim controller to adjust this coefficient to correct for variations in the physical properties and heater efficiency. However, these parameters are not expected to vary much, which means that the feedback trim controller would have to be detuned (low gain, slow reset, and no derivative) so that it does not change the coefficient very drastically during the transient error of the feedforward controller. A better control system structure results if the feedback controller output is made to adjust the set point of the feedforward controller or, equivalently, the product of the unknown coefficient and the set point, as follows:

$$F^{set} = \left[m - \frac{C}{H_v\text{Eff}} T_i \right]W \qquad (8\text{-}14)$$

where $m = CT_o^{set}/(H_vEff)$ is the output of the feedback controller, and the coefficient C/H_vEff becomes the tunable gain of the inlet temperature correction. Notice that this term can be calculated from measured values of the temperatures and flows, averaged over long enough periods of time. From Eq. (8-13):

$$\frac{C}{H_vEff} = \frac{F}{W(T_o - T_i)} \tag{8-15}$$

7. The design formula was derived from a steady-state energy balance on the heater. Dynamic compensation will probably be required, because changes in steam flow (the manipulated variable) are delayed by the lags of the control valve and the steam chest, while the process flow will have a faster effect on the outlet temperature, and the inlet temperature will be delayed by the transportation lag in the heater. To compensate for these dynamic imbalances, lead-lag units can be inserted on the two measured disturbances before they are used in the computation.

8. Figure 8-10 shows the instrumentation diagram for the feedforward controller. In some computer control systems, the multiplier may be carried out as a ratio controller, with

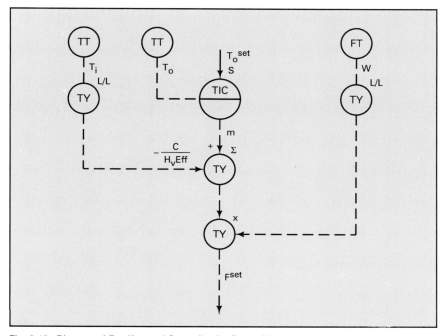

Fig. 8-10. Diagram of Feedforward Controller for Steam Heater.

the ratio being set by the summer that combines the feedback controller output and the inlet temperature correction.

Example 8-2, Effect of Lead-Lag Compensation: Compare the response of the feedforward controller of the preceding example with and without lead-lag compensation.

Figure 8-11 shows the response of the outlet temperature to a change in process flow with lead-lag compensation and without it (static compensation). For comparison, the line of crosses shows what the temperature would do if the steam flow were kept constant. The static compensation response shows that, even though the steam is immediately increased in proportion to the process flow, the heater outlet temperature still drops. This indicates that the steam flow must lead the process flow. Assume a net lead of 1 min is required. As the process flow is expected to be a noisy signal, specify a lead of

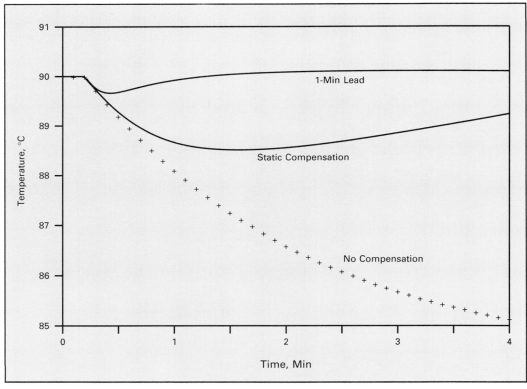

Fig. 8-11. Effect of Lead on the Response of the Outlet Temperature of the Steam Heater to a 2 kg/s Increase in Process Flow.

3 minutes and a lag of 2 minutes, so that the noise is amplified only by a factor of 3/2 = 1.5. Figure 8-11 shows that the net lead of 1 min significantly reduces the drop in temperature caused by the rise in process flow.

Figure 8-12 shows the response of the outlet temperature to a 10°C increase in inlet temperature with and without lead-lag compensation. Once again, for comparison, the line of crosses shows the uncompensated response. The fact that the static compensation response is in the opposite direction from the uncompensated response says that the correction in steam flow is too fast, and, therefore, the steam flow must lag the inlet temperature. Figure 8-12 shows that a lag of 1 min (with zero lead) keeps the temperature from dropping. In this case, dead time compensation could have been used, as the dead time to inlet temperature (the disturbance) is longer than the dead time to the steam flow (the manipulated variable).

The preceding example has a characteristic typical of many successful feedforward control applications: the formulas used

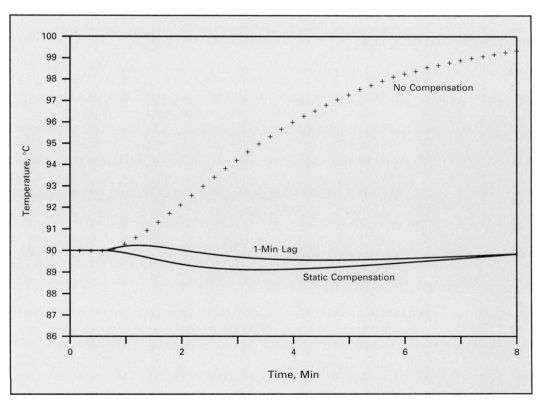

Fig. 8-12. Effect of Lag on the Response of the Outlet Temperature of the Steam Heater to a 10°C Increase in Inlet Temperature.

in the compensation are simple steady-state relationships. If dynamic compensation is needed, lead-lag and dead time compensation algorithms are added to the nonlinear steady-state compensator. The moral is: keep the design super simple.

8-5. Summary

Ratio and feedforward control complement feedback control by preventing deviations of the controlled variable caused by disturbances. The feedforward controller is free of stability considerations but requires a model of the process to be controlled. The best approach is a combination of feedforward and feedback control. Ratio control is the simplest form of feedforward control; it establishes a simple proportionality between two flows.

Exercises

8-1. *Why isn't it possible to have perfect control—the variable always equal to the set point—with feedback control alone? Is perfect control possible with feedforward control?*

8-2. *What are the main requirements of feedforward control? What are the advantages of feedforward control with feedback trim over pure feedforward control?*

8-3. *What is ratio control? What is the control objective of the air-to-natural gas ratio controller in the control system sketched in Fig. 7-5 for the ammonia process? Which are the measured disturbance and the manipulated variable for that ratio controller?*

8-4. *What is a lead-lag unit? How is it used in a feedforward control scheme? Describe the step and ramp responses of a lead-lag unit.*

8-5. *It is desired to lead a disturbance in a feedforward controller by 1.5 minutes. If the amplification factor for the noise in the disturbance measurement must not exceed 2, what must the lead and the lag be?*

8-6. *What is dead time compensation in a feedforward controller? When can it be used? When should it be used?*

8-7. *Design a feedforward controller to compensate for changes in process flow, inlet temperature, and supplementary fuel flow in the outlet temperature control of the furnace shown in the figure. Explicitly discuss each of the eight steps of the procedure outlined in the text.*

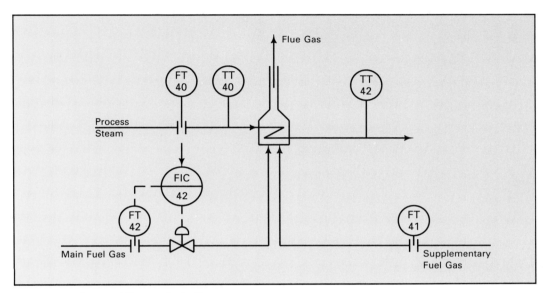

Feedforward Control of Furnace Outlet Temperature.

References

1. Luyben, W. L., *Process Modeling, Simulation, and Control for Chemical Engineers*, 2nd ed. (New York: McGraw-Hill, 1990).
2. Shinskey, F. G., "Feedforward Control Applied," *ISA Journal* (Nov. 1963), p. 61.
3. Smith, C. A., and Corripio, A. B., *Principles and Practice of Automatic Process Control* (New York: Wiley, 1985), section 8-4.

Unit 9:
Multivariable Control Systems

UNIT 9

Multivariable Control Systems

Previous units have regarded the tuning of feedback controllers from a single-loop point of view; that is, a single control objective and a single manipulated variable are considered at a time. This unit examines the effect on the performance and tuning of a control loop when other loops are switched from manual to automatic or vice versa, or when their tuning is changed. To do this the control problem must be viewed with multiple objectives, that is, the multivariable control problem.

Learning Objectives — When you have completed this unit you should:

A. Understand how interaction with other loops affects the performance of a feedback control loop.

B. Be able to calculate the steady-state interaction between loops.

C. Pair controlled and manipulated variables so that the effect of interaction is minimized.

D. Adjust the tuning of feedback controllers to account for interaction.

E. Design decouplers so that the performance of a loop becomes independent of the state (manual or automatic) of other loops.

9-1. What Is Loop Interaction?

When two or more feedback loops are installed on a process or unit operation (e.g., distillation column, evaporator, etc.), the possibility of interaction between the loops arises. This means that each controlled variable is affected by more than one manipulated variable, as shown in Fig. 9-1, where, in controlling the total flow and concentration of a simple blender, both controlled variables are affected by each of the two manipulated variables (the flows of the concentrated and dilute streams). The problem that arises is known as loop interaction. Since multiple control objectives are involved, the problem can also be seen as the design of a multivariable control system.

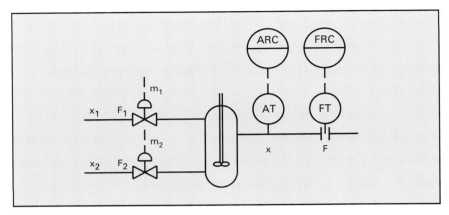

Fig. 9-1. Multivariable Control of a Blender.

Effect of Loop Interaction

Consider the block diagram representation of the 2 × 2 multivariable control system given in Fig. 9-2. The terms G_{11} and G_{21} are the process transfer functions of manipulated variable M_1 on the two controlled variables C_1 and C_2, while G_{12} and G_{22} are the corresponding transfer functions for manipulated variable M_2. The two controller transfer functions, G_{C1} and G_{C2}, act on their respective errors, E_1 and E_2, to produce the two manipulated variables. Signals R_1 and R_2 represent the set points of the loops. In the diagram of Fig. 9-2 the process transfer functions include the gains and dynamics of the final control elements (valves), the process,

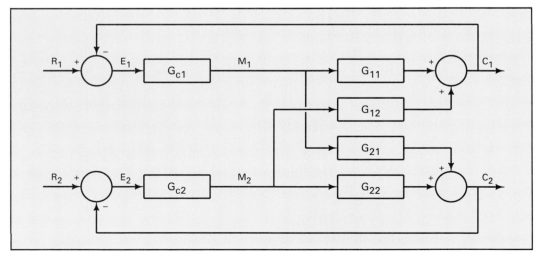

Fig. 9-2. Block Diagram for a 2 × 2 Interacting Control System.

and the sensor/transmitters. For simplicity, the disturbances are not shown.

To look at the effect of interaction, assume that the gains of all four process blocks are positive; that is, an increase in each manipulated variable results in an increase in each of the controlled variables. Suppose then that at a point in time a step change is applied in manipulated variable M_1 with both loops on manual (opened). The responses of both controlled variables, C_1 and C_2, are shown in Fig. 9-3, where the time of the step change is marked as point a. Now suppose that at time b control loop 2 is closed (switched to automatic) and that it has integral or reset mode. Manipulated variable M_2 will be decreased until controlled variable C_2 comes back down to its original value, assumed to be its set point. The decrease in M_2 also causes, through interaction block G_{12}, a decrease in controlled variable C_1, so that the net change in C_1 is smaller than the initial change. Notice that this initial change is the only change that would take place if there were no interaction or if controller 2 were kept on manual. The difference between the initial change and the net change in C_1 is the effect of interaction. It depends on the effect that M_1 has on C_2 (G_{21}); the effect that M_2 has on C_2 (G_{22}, which

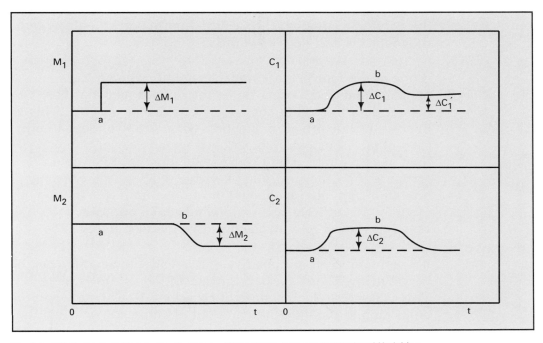

Fig. 9-3. Effect of Interaction on the Response of the Controlled and Manipulated Variables.

determines the necessary corrective action on M_2); and the effect that M_2 has on C_1 (G_{12}). Notice that the steady-state effect of interaction depends only on the process transfer functions, not on the controller tuning, when controller 2 has integral mode.

For practice, verify that a step in M_2, followed by closing control loop 1, has the same effect on C_2, at least qualitatively, as has just been observed for C_1. It will be shown shortly that the relative effect of interaction is quantitatively the same for control loop 2 as it is for control loop 1.

In the case just analyzed, it was assumed that all four process transfer functions had positive gains (direct actions). The effect of interaction was in the opposite direction from the direct (initial) effect of the step change, resulting in a net change that was smaller than the initial change. This type of situation in which the two loops "fight each other" is known as "negative" interaction. It can be easily verified that, if any two of the process transfer functions had positive gains and the other two had negative gains, the interaction would also be negative. Notice that it is possible for the effect of interaction to be greater than the initial effect, in which case the net change will be in the opposite direction from the initial change. Here it can be said that "the wrong loop wins the fight"—a situation that results from incorrect pairing of the loops, as will be seen shortly.

If one of the four process transfer functions had a sign opposite that of the other three, the net change would be greater than the initial change, as can also be verified. This is the case of "positive" interaction when the two loops "help each other". Positive interaction is usually easier to handle than negative interaction because the possibility of inverse response (i.e., the controlled variable moving in the wrong direction right after a change) or of open-loop overshoot, both of which result from two parallel effects in opposite directions, exist only in the negative interaction case.

It is evident that both positive and negative interaction can be very detrimental to the performance of the control system. This is because the response of each loop is affected when the other loop is switched into and out of automatic or when its output saturates.

In summary, the following are key characteristics of loop interaction:

1. For interaction to affect the performance of the control system, it must work both ways; that is, each manipulated variable must affect both controlled variables through the process. (Notice that if either G_{12} or G_{21} are absent from the diagram of Fig. 9-2, there is no interaction effect.)
2. Because of interaction, a set point change to either loop produces at least a transitory change in both controlled variables.
3. The interaction effect on one loop can be eliminated by interrupting the other loop; that is, if one of the two controllers is switched to "manual," the remaining loop is no longer affected by interaction.

The following sections present two ways to approach the problem of loop interaction:

1. Pair the controlled and manipulated variables to minimize the effect of interaction between the loops.
2. Combine the controller output signals through decouplers to eliminate the interaction between the loops.

Some advanced multivariable control design techniques are based on control strategies other than the standard PID control algorithm, notably Dynamic Matrix Control (DMC), Internal Model Control (IMC), and others. References on these techniques appear at the end of this unit.

9-2. Pairing of Controlled and Manipulated Variables

Usually, the first step in the design of a control system for a process is the selection of the control loops, that is, the selection of those variables that must be controlled and those variables that are to be manipulated to control them. This pairing task has been traditionally performed by the process engineer and based primarily on his or her intuition and knowledge of the process. Fortunately, for many loops, intuition is all that is necessary. However, when the interactions involved in a system are not clearly understood and the "intuitive" approach produces the wrong pairing, control performance is poor. The expedient solution is then to switch the troublesome controllers to manual, which, as pointed out in the preceding section, eliminates the effect of interaction. The many controllers operating in manual in control rooms throughout the industry are a testimony to the failures in correctly pairing the variables in the system; each is a failure of an attempt to apply automatic control.

A method to quantitatively determine the correct pairing of controlled and manipulated variables in a multivariable system was published by Bristol (Reference 1). It is popularly known as the Relative Gain Matrix or Interaction Measure, and it requires only steady-state information that is easy to obtain off-line. The fact that dynamic information is not included is the one objection that has kept the method from being accepted more widely.

Open-Loop Gains

Consider the 2×2 system of Fig. 9-2. If a change is applied to manipulated variable M_1, keeping the other manipulated variable constant, and the changes in controlled variables C_1 and C_2 are measured, the following open-loop gains can be calculated:

$$K_{11} = \left.\frac{\Delta C_1}{\Delta M_1}\right|_{M_2\,const.} \quad K_{21} = \left.\frac{\Delta C_2}{\Delta M_1}\right|_{M_2\,const.} \tag{9-1}$$

Similarly, when a change is applied to M_2, keeping M_1 constant, the other two open-loop gains can be calculated:

$$K_{12} = \left.\frac{\Delta C_1}{\Delta M_2}\right|_{M_1\,const.} \quad K_{22} = \left.\frac{\Delta C_2}{\Delta M_2}\right|_{M_1\,const.} \tag{9-2}$$

The open-loop gains can also be obtained from the steady-state equations or computer simulation programs used to design the plant.

There is a natural tendency to try to use the open-loop gains in the pairing of the variables. However, it is immediately apparent that C_1 and C_2 and M_1 and M_2 do not necessarily have the same dimensions. Thus, attempting to compare open-loop gains would be the same as trying to decide between buying a new sofa or a new house. To overcome this problem, Bristol (Reference 1) proposes to compute relative gains that are independent of dimensions.

Closed-Loop Gains

Because of interaction, the effect that M_1 has on C_1 is different when the other loop is closed than when it is opened (see the previous section). The "closed-loop gain" for the pairing M_1-C_1 is defined as:

$$K'_{11} = \frac{\Delta C'_1}{\Delta M_1}\bigg|_{C_2 \text{const.}} \tag{9-3}$$

This closed-loop gain can be computed from the open-loop gains previously defined. The total change in C_1 is given by:

$$\Delta C'_1 = K_{11}\Delta M_1 + K_{12}\Delta M_2 \tag{9-4}$$

The change in M_2 required to keep C_2 at its set point can be computed as follows:

$$\Delta C_2 = K_{21}\Delta M_1 + K_{22}\Delta M_2 = 0 \tag{9-5}$$

$$\Delta M_2 = -\frac{K_{21}}{K_{22}}\Delta M_1 \tag{9-6}$$

Substitution of Eq. (9-6) into Eq. (9-4) and then into Eq. (9-3) results in the following formula for the closed-loop gain:

$$K'_{11} = K_{11} - \frac{K_{12}K_{21}}{K_{22}} \tag{9-7}$$

The closed-loop gains for each of the other three pairings can be similarly derived.

Relative Gains (Interaction Measure)

Bristol's relative gains are obtained by dividing each open-loop gain by the corresponding closed-loop gain:

$$\mu_{ij} = \frac{K_{ij}}{K'_{ij}} \tag{9-8}$$

where μ_{ij} is the relative gain for the pairing of controller variable C_i with manipulated variable M_j.

The following formulas can be used to compute the relative gains for any 2 × 2 system:

$$\mu_{11} = \mu_{22} = \frac{K_{11}K_{22}}{K_{11}K_{22} - K_{12}K_{21}} \qquad (9\text{-}9)$$

$$\mu_{12} = \mu_{21} = \frac{K_{12}K_{21}}{K_{12}K_{21} - K_{11}K_{22}} \qquad (9\text{-}10)$$

It makes sense that the interaction measure for the C_1-M_1 pair be the same as for the C_2-M_2 pair, as they represent a single option in the 2 × 2 system, the other option being C_1-M_2 and C_2-M_1.

The relative gains are dimensionless and can, therefore, be compared to one another. The comparison is performed by arranging the gains in a matrix called the Relative Gain Matrix (RGM):

	M_1	M_2
C_1	μ_{11}	μ_{12}
C_2	μ_{21}	μ_{22}

$(9\text{-}11)$

The variables are paired so that the relative gain for the pair is closest to unity, as this will result in the minimum effect of interaction for the particular process. Notice that, for the case of no interaction, the open-loop gain is equal to the closed-loop gain, and the relative gains are 1.0 for one pairing and 0.0 for the other.

Example 9-1, Calculation of the Relative Gains: Consider a process for which the open-loop gains are:

	M_1	M_2
C_1	1.0	1.0
C_2	−0.1	0.4

The relative gains are, from Eqs. (9-9) through (9-10):

$$\mu_{11} = \mu_{22} = (1.0)(0.4)/[(1.0)(0.4) - (-0.1)(1.0)] = 0.8$$

$$\mu_{12} = \mu_{21} = (-0.1)(1.0)/[(-0.1)(1.0) - (1.0)(0.4)] = 0.2$$

This means that if M_1 is paired with C_1 and M_2 with C_2, the steady-state gain of each loop increases by 1/0.8 or 25% when the other loop is closed. If, alternatively, M_1 is paired with C_2 and M_2 with C_1, the gain of each loop increases by a factor of $1/0.2 = 5$ (400% increase) when the other loop is closed! Obviously, one pairing is significantly less sensitive to interaction than the other.

Extension to Systems with More than Two Control Objectives

Equations (9-9) and (9-10) can be used to compute the relative gains for any 2×2 system. For systems with more than two controlled and manipulated variables, the definition of the relative gains is still the ratio of the open-loop gain to the closed-loop gain for a pair of controlled and manipulated variables:

$$\mu_{ij} = \frac{K_{ij}}{K'_{ij}} = \frac{\Delta C_i / \Delta M_j | \text{all other M's const.}}{\Delta C'_i / \Delta M_j | \text{all other C's const.}} \qquad (9\text{-}12)$$

The calculation of the relative gains is straightforward, but it involves the inversion of the matrix of open-loop gains. It is, therefore, helpful to use a computer and "canned" programs to perform the following matrix operations:

1. Compute the inverse of the matrix of open-loop gains.
2. Transpose the inverse matrix.
3. Multiply each term of the open-loop gain matrix by the corresponding term of the transposed inverse matrix to obtain the corresponding term of the relative gain matrix.

Properties of the Relative Gains

1. The relative gains are not only nondimensional but they are also normalized in the sense that the sum of the gains of any row or column of the matrix is unity. This fact can be verified for the 2×2 system by adding the relative gain formulas for each pairing [that is, Eqs. (9-9) and (9-10)]. This property also applies to systems with more than two controlled and manipulated variables.
2. Positive and Negative Interaction. For the 2×2 system, when the two loops help each other (positive interaction), the relative gains are between 0 and 1; when the two loops fight each other (negative interaction), one set of relative gains is greater than unity and the other set is negative. Notice that a negative relative gain means that the net

action of the loop reverses when the other loop is opened or closed—a very undesirable situation.

For a system with more than two control objectives, the concept of positive and negative interaction must be applied on a pair-by-pair basis. If the relative gain for a pair of controlled and manipulated variables is positive and less than unity, the interaction is positive (that pair is "helped" by the interaction of all the other loops). On the other hand, if the relative gain for a pair is greater than unity or negative, the interaction is negative (the combined action of all other loops causes a change in the controlled variable that is in the opposite direction from the direct change caused by the manipulated variable in the pair).

For most processes the relative gain matrix tells all that is needed to know about interaction from the open-loop steady-state gains, which are easy to determine both on-line and off-line. However, as shall be seen in the distillation column example, if the step response of the process is non-monotonic (inverse response or open-loop overshoot), the pairing recommended by relative gain analysis may not result in the best control performance because it does not consider the dynamic response.

Example 9-2, Control of Composition and Flow in a Catalyst Blender: Consider the blender of Fig. 9-1 where the objectives are to control the composition (x) and the flow (F) of the product stream. The positions of the control valves on the two feed streams can be manipulated. Which of the two controllers should be paired to which valve to minimize the effect of interaction? Use the interaction measure to determine this. (Note: Although ratio control should be used here, this still leaves the question of which flow should be ratioed to which, and the answer to the original question will also answer this one. In fact, the ratio controller is really a form of decoupling here.)

The following open-loop relationships are obtained from the steady-state mass and component balances for the blender:

Mass balance: $\qquad\qquad\qquad F = F_1 + F_2$

Component balance: $\qquad\quad x = (F_1 x_1 + F_2 x_2)/(F_1 + F_2)$

Differential calculus can then be used to determine the steady-state gains:

$$K_{11} = \frac{\Delta F}{\Delta M_1}\bigg|_{M_2 const.} = K_{v1} \qquad K_{12} = \frac{\Delta F}{\Delta M_2}\bigg|_{M_1 const.} = K_{v2}$$

$$K_{21} = \frac{\Delta x}{\Delta M_1}\bigg|_{M_2 const.} = \frac{F_2(x_1 - x_2)}{(F_1 + F_2)^2} K_{v1}$$

$$K_{22} = \frac{\Delta x}{\Delta M_2}\bigg|_{M_1 const.} = \frac{F_1(x_2 - x_1)}{(F_1 + F_2)^2} K_{v2}$$

where K_{v1} and K_{v2} are the valve gains, in (lb/min)/fraction valve position.

Next, substitute the open-loop gains into the formulas for the relative gains, Eqs. (9-9) and (9-10). After a little algebraic manipulation, the following general expressions for the relative gains are obtained:

	M_1	M_2
F	F_1/F	F_2/F
x	F_2/F	F_1/F

In words, the pairing that minimizes interaction has the flow controller manipulating the larger of the two flows and the composition controller manipulating the smaller of the two flows. If a ratio controller were to be used, the smaller flow must be ratioed to the larger flow, with the flow controller manipulating the larger flow and the composition controller manipulating the ratio. It could easily be shown that the ratio controller decouples the two loops so that a change in flow does not affect the composition.

Example 9-3, Two-Point Composition Control of a Distillation Column: Figure 9-4 shows a sketch of a distillation column with five manipulated and controlled variables. The column separates a 50% mixture of benzene and toluene into a distillate product with 95% benzene and bottoms product with 5% benzene. The two main objectives are to maintain the compositions of the distillate and bottoms product at their set points. The two temperature controllers (TRC 1 and TRC 2) serve as inferential measurements of composition. The three

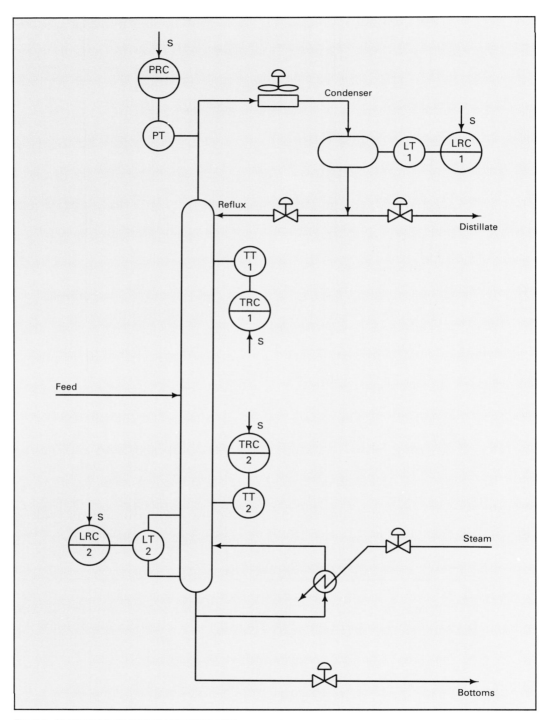

Fig. 9-4. Multivariable Control of a Distillation Column.

secondary objectives are to maintain the vapor balance by controlling the column pressure (PRC) and the liquid balances by controlling the levels in the accumulator drum (LRC 1) and column bottom (LRC 2). The possible manipulated variables are the flow rates of the two products, the reflux, the steam to the reboiler, and the cooling rate of the condenser.

The two level variables do not affect the operation of the column directly, thus they cannot be made a part of the interaction analysis. However, the decision about which streams control the levels has an effect on the interaction between the other control loops. Two such arrangements will be considered. To reduce the problem to a two by two, assume that the pressure controller manipulates the condenser cooling rate.

Scheme 1. Level Control by Product Stream Manipulation.

In this scheme, commonly known as "Energy Balance Control," the distillate rate is manipulated to control the level in the condenser accumulator (LRC 1), and the bottoms rate is manipulated to control the bottom level (LRC 2), as shown in Fig. 9-5. This leaves two unpaired control loops: the two temperature controllers with the steam and reflux rates.

The following results were obtained from sensitivity tests performed on a simulation of the column at Louisiana State University's installation of IBM's Advanced Control System (ACS):

Open-Loop Gains:

	Reflux	Steam
TRC 1	−2.85	1.16
TRC 2	−0.438	2.53

Relative Gains:

	Reflux	Steam
TRC 1	3.38	−2.38
TRC 2	−2.38	3.38

Notice that the obvious pairing (top temperature with reflux and bottom temperature with steam) results in less interaction than the other. Even so, there is much interaction between the two loops: a decrease of the gain of each loop by a factor of 3.38 when the other loop is switched to automatic, indicating that the two temperature loops fight each other. This scheme suffers, therefore, from negative interaction.

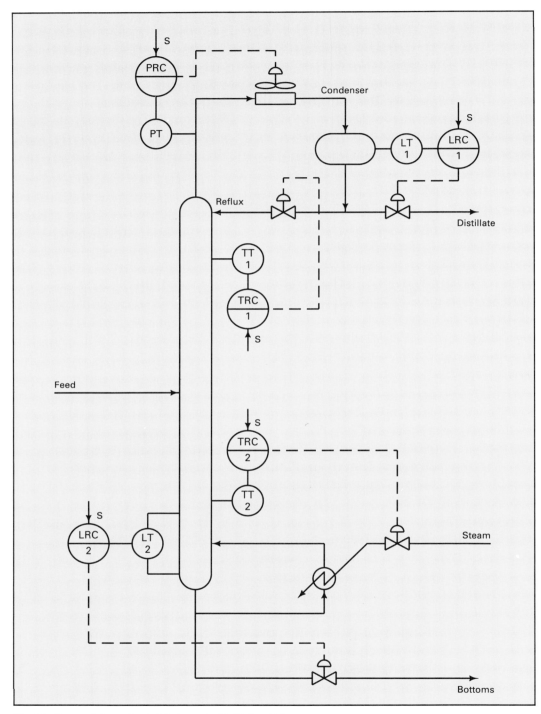

Fig. 9-5. Energy Balance Control Scheme for Distillation Column.

Scheme 2. Bottom Level by Steam Manipulation.

In this scheme, known as "Direct Material Balance Control," the bottom level is controlled by manipulating the steam rate and the bottom temperature by manipulating the bottoms product rate, as shown in Fig. 9-6. The top of the column remains the same as before. The loops to be paired involve the two temperature controllers with the bottoms rate and the reflux.

The sensitivity study on the simulated column gives the following open-loop and relative gains:

Open-Loop Gains:			**Relative Gains:**		
	Reflux	Bottoms		Reflux	Bottoms
TRC 1	−0.35	−1.05	TRC 1	0.90	0.10
TRC 2	0.07	−1.93	TRC 2	0.10	0.90

The pairing for this scheme is also the obvious one (top temperature with reflux and bottom temperature with bottoms product flow); the relative gains show only about 10% positive interaction (that is, the two loops help each other), indicated by the relative gains being positive and less than unity.

It would appear, then, from steady-state relative gain analysis that Direct Material Balance Control results in significantly less interaction than Energy Balance Control. Unfortunately, the Energy Balance Control scheme, which is shown to have more steady-state interaction by relative gain analysis, was found to perform better in this particular case than the Direct Material Balance Control scheme. The reason is dynamic interaction that goes undetected by the relative gain matrix. For the first scheme the open-loop responses are monotonic; that is, the temperature stays between its initial value and its final value during the entire response. On the other hand, for the second scheme the open-loop responses exhibit inverse response; that is, the temperature moves in one direction at the beginning of the response and then moves back to a final value on the opposite side of its initial value. This causes the feedback controller to initially take action in the wrong direction, degrading the performance of the control system.

Although in this particular example relative gain analysis fails to properly predict which of the two control schemes performs

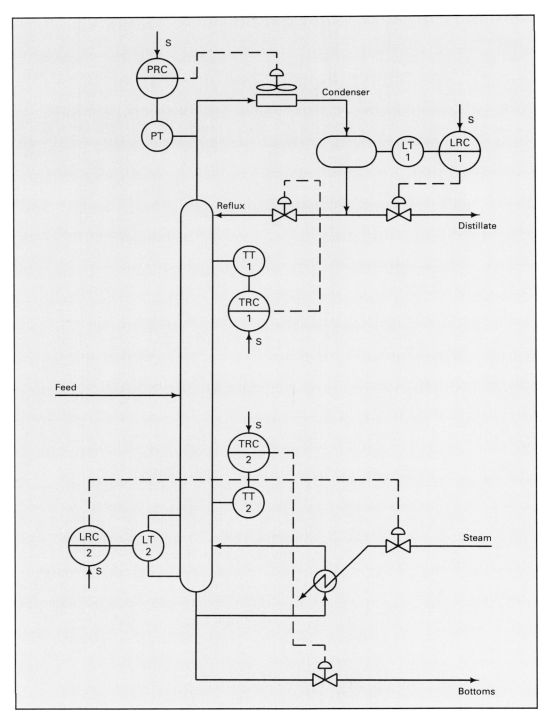

Fig. 9-6. Direct Material Balance Control of Bottoms Product.

better, it is still useful in verifying that the intuitive pairing is the correct one for each scheme. It would have also evaluated the interaction for each scheme correctly had all the responses been monotonic.

This example shows that the arrangement of the level controllers affects the interaction between the other loops in the column.

9-3. Design and Tuning of Decouplers

Although relative gain analysis usually results in the pairing of variables that minimizes the effect of loop interaction, it does not eliminate it. When the terms of the relative gain matrix (RGM) approach 0.5, the effect of interaction is the same regardless of the pairing. In the case of negative interaction when one set of relative gains is negative and the other much greater than unity, the proper pairing still produces much interaction. The only solution to this problem is to compensate for interaction by designing a decoupler.

A decoupler is a signal processor that combines the controller outputs to produce the signals to the control valves or slave controller set points. Its operation can best be understood by considering the block diagram of a decoupled 2 × 2 system shown in Fig. 9-7.

Each of the two decoupler terms, D_1 and D_2, can be considered to be feedforward controllers for which the "disturbances" are the controller output signals U_1 and U_2. The design of the decouplers is, therefore, identical to the design of a feedforward controller discussed in Unit 8.

Decoupler Design Formulas

The objective of decoupler term D_1 is to compensate for the effect of U_2 on C_1, that is, to prevent changes in the output of the second controller from affecting the controlled variable of the first loop:

$$\Delta C_1 = D_1 G_{11} \Delta U_2 + G_{12} \Delta U_2 = 0 \qquad (9\text{-}13)$$

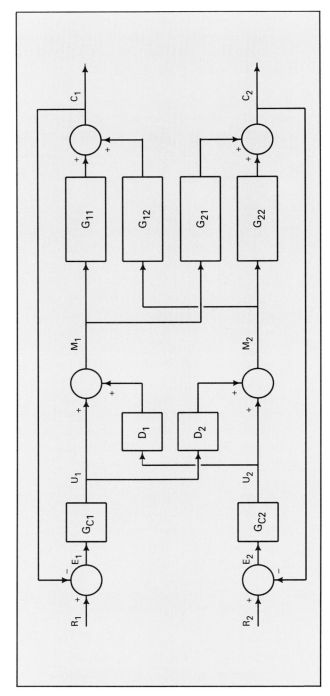

Fig. 9-7. Block Diagram of Decoupled 2 × 2 Control System.

From the preceding design requirement, the transfer function of the decoupler term can be determined:

$$D_1 = -\frac{G_{12}}{G_{11}} \qquad (9\text{-}14)$$

Similarly, the decoupler term D_2 is designed to compensate for the effect of U_1 on C_2, and, from the block diagram of Fig. 9-7, the following transfer function is obtained:

$$D_2 = -\frac{G_{21}}{G_{22}} \qquad (9\text{-}15)$$

Decoupling, like feedforward, can be designed to varied degrees of complexity. The simplest is given by linear static compensation (i.e., forfeiting the dynamic compensation), which can be accomplished in practice by a simple summer with adjustable gains. The next degree of complexity is to add dynamic compensation in the form of lead-lag units (see Unit 8). Ultimately, nonlinear models of the process could be used to design nonlinear decouplers, following the procedure outlined in Unit 8. Notice that the derivation of Eqs. (9-14) and (9-15) has been based on linear models.

Decoupling and Control Loop Performance

Unlike feedforward controllers, the decoupler forms a part of the feedback loop and as such can introduce instability in the system. Consider the total effects that U_1 has on C_1 and that U_2 has on C_2:

$$\frac{\Delta C_1}{\Delta U_1} = G_{11} + D_2 G_{12} \qquad (9\text{-}16)$$

$$\frac{\Delta C_2}{\Delta U_2} = G_{22} + D_1 G_{21} \qquad (9\text{-}17)$$

It is possible for dynamic compensation to call for unstable poles in D_1 and D_2. These poles must obviously be left out of the decouplers to maintain stability.

Another aspect of decoupling is that, as is evident from Eqs. (9-16) and (9-17), there are two parallel paths between each controller output and its controlled variable. For processes with negative interaction, these two parallel paths will have opposite signs, creating either an inverse response or an overshoot in the open-loop step response of each decoupled loop. However, it is important to realize that the parallel paths are not created by the decouplers; they were already present in the undecoupled system (the interaction and direct effects).

It is evident from the design of the decoupler that the steady-state effect of the decoupler on any one loop is the same as the integral action the other loops would have if the decoupler were not used. What then does the decoupler achieve? Basically, through decoupling, the effect of interaction is made independent of whether the other loops are opened or closed. However, problems may still arise in one loop if the manipulated variable of another loop is driven to the limits of its range, because the decoupling action is then blocked by saturation.

It is, therefore, important to select the correct pairing of manipulated and controlled variables even when decoupling is used, so that saturation of one of the manipulated variables in the multivariable system would not drastically affect the performance of the other loops.

Half Decoupling

As seen earlier, the interaction effect depends on both manipulated variables affecting both controlled variables. Thus, interaction can be eliminated by decoupling one loop and letting the other loop be affected, that is, implementing either D_1 or D_2 but not both. In deciding which decoupler to select, one consideration may be which of the controlled variables is more important to keep at its set point. Another consideration may be the ease with which the dynamic terms of the decouplers can be implemented.

In summary, decoupling is a viable strategy for multivariable control systems. Its design is similar to feedforward control, although simpler in that it does not require additional measurements of process variables. Unlike feedforward, the decoupler forms part of the loop response and affects its stability. Applications of decoupling are usually restricted to 2×2 systems. More sophisticated control strategies are used with systems involving more than two control objectives.

Example 9-4, Design a Decoupler for the Catalyst Blender:
The two objectives of the control system for the catalyst

blender of Fig. 9-1 are the control of the product composition
and flow. Since the blender is full of liquid, the response of
the total flow to changes in each of the input flows is
instantaneous; thus, the decoupler for the total flow should
not require dynamic compensation. The response of the
product composition should be that of a first-order lag with a
time constant equal to the residence time of the tank—volume
divided by the total flow. Since this time constant is the same
for the composition response to either input flow, dynamic
compensation should not be required for the composition
decoupler.

The application of the linear decoupler design formulas, Eqs.
(9-14) and (9-15), results in the following formulas for the
signals to the control valves, assuming that F_1 is the larger of
the two flows, and, for minimum interaction, it is used to
control the total flow, as was determined by relative gain
analysis in Example 9-2:

$$M_1 = U_1 - \frac{K_{v2}}{K_{v1}} (U_2 - U_{2o})$$

$$M_2 = U_2 + \frac{F_2 K_{v1}}{F_1 K_{v2}} (U_1 - U_{1o})$$

where U_{1o} and U_{2o} are the controller outputs at initialization.

The coefficients correct for the sizes of the two valves and, in
the second formula, for the ratio between the two inlet flows,
which is required to maintain the composition constant. This
ratio is a function of the two inlet stream compositions and
the product composition set point. If any of these
compositions were to vary, the gain of the decoupler would
have to be readjusted. However, another way to design the
decoupler does not require readjustment of the parameters
when process conditions change; it consists of using simple
process models to set up the structure of the control system.

Decoupler Design from Process Models

The total mass balance and the component balance on the
blender given in Example 9-2 provide the models needed to
design the decouplers. From the total mass balance it can be
determined that the output of the product flow controller

should manipulate the sum of the two inlet flows, so the output of the flow controller is set equal to the total inlet flow, and the smaller flow subtracted from it to determine the larger flow:

$$F_1^{set} = U_1 - F_2$$

This formula requires the measurement of the smaller flow and flow control of the larger flow.

The component mass balance shows that the product composition depends on the ratio of the flows rather than on any one of the inlet flows. Therefore, the output of the composition controller is set equal to the ratio of the smaller flow to the larger flow, and the smaller flow calculated as follows:

$$F_2^{set} = U_2 F_1$$

This formula requires that the smaller flow also be controlled. The diagram of the resulting control system is shown in Fig. 9-8. In this scheme the ratio controller keeps the product

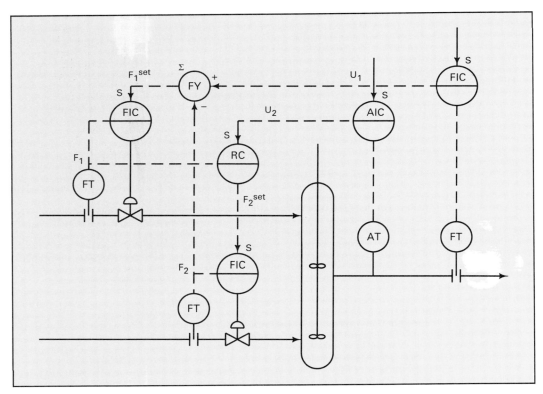

Fig. 9-8. Decoupled Control System for Catalyst Blender of Fig. 9-1.

composition from changing when the total flow is changed, and the summer keeps the total flow from changing when the composition controller takes action. The multivariable control system is, therefore, fully decoupled.

The last two design formulas do not show the scale factors that may be necessary to convert the flow signals into percent of the scales of the flow controllers. The scale factors depend on the spans of the two flow transmitters rather than on the sizes of the control valves. The flow controllers allow the signals to be linear with flow and also take care of changes in pressure drop across the control valves.

9-4. Tuning of Multivariable Control Systems

It is obvious from the analysis of interacting loops that the interaction is going to affect the response of each loop; that is, the tuning parameters and manual/automatic state of each loop affect how the other loops respond. This section explains how to account for the effect of interaction when tuning each loop in a multivariable control system.

The first thing to do when tuning interacting loops is prioritize the control objectives: rank the controlled variables in the order of importance in regard to maintaining them at their set points. Then the relative gain for the most important variable is checked to decide whether to detune the other loops. The principle behind this approach is that a loosely tuned feedback control loop (low gain and slow reset) will behave as if it were opened; or, rather, it will make slow enough changes in its manipulated variable to allow the controller of the important variable to correct for the effect of interaction. The decision on how loosely to tune the less important loops is based on how different from unity the relative gain is for the most important loop. It is understood that the manipulated variable for the most important variable has been selected to make the relative gain for that loop as close to unity as possible. When there are more than two interacting loops, the tightness of tuning for each loop will decrease with its rank.

An alternate approach to detuning the less important loops is to install decouplers that compensate for the effect of the action of the less important loops on the most important loop. The decouplers that compensate for the action of the most important loop on the other loops should not be installed, especially if the relative gain for that loop is greater than unity. This is because, as was seen in the preceding section in the analysis of the decoupled block diagram of Fig. 9-7, the action of the decoupler affects the loop whose action is compensated for. If the relative gain for a loop is greater than unity or negative (negative interaction), the decoupler action will be in the opposite direction from the direct action of the manipulated variable, causing inverse response or overshoot, which makes the loop less controllable. Notice that, for loops with negative interaction, detuning the other loops will slow down the parallel effect in the opposite direction if the decoupler is not used. Thus, for example, if the top loop in Fig. 9-7 were the most important of the two, decoupler D_1 would be used but not decoupler D_2.

If at least two of the control objectives in a multivariable control system are of equal importance, they should be tuned as tightly as possible. In such a case, they should be tuned in the order of decreasing speed of response. If one of the important control loops can be tuned to respond much faster than the others, it should be tuned first and be kept in automatic while the other loops are tuned. In this manner, the response used for tuning the slower loops will include the interaction effect of the faster loop. For example, in the control system for the blender of Fig. 9-1, the flow controller should be faster than the composition controller because the flow responds almost instantaneously, while the composition is lagged by the time constant of the tank. The flow controller must then be tuned first and be kept in automatic while the composition controller is tuned.

If all of the loops are of equal importance and speed of response, a simple approach is to tune each loop while the other loops are in manual; then, the gain of each loop is adjusted by multiplying the gain obtained when all other loops were opened by the relative gain for the loop:

$$K'_{cij} = K_{cij}\mu_{ij} \tag{9-18}$$

where:

K'_{cij} = the adjusted controller gain

K_{cij} = the controller gain tuned with all the other loops opened

μ_{ij} = the relative gain for the loop

This adjustment will account for the change in steady-state gain when the other loops are closed, but it will not account for dynamic effects. If some of the loops are slower than the others or can be detuned, the relative gains for the remaining loops must be recalculated as if those were the only interacting loops (as if the slower or detuned loops were always opened).

The gain adjustment suggested by Eq. (9-18) should be sufficient for those loops with positive interaction, as their response should remain monotonic when the other loops are closed. However, the loops with negative interaction may require retuning after the other loops are closed, because the other loops will cause either inverse or overshoot response, which normally requires lower gains and slower reset than monotonic (minimum phase) loops. Notice that the formula will result in a gain reduction for the loops with positive interaction and a gain increase for the loops with negative interaction, assuming the pairing with the positive relative gain is always used.

When decouplers are used, they must be tuned first and be kept active while the feedback controllers are tuned. Recall that perfect decoupling has the same effect on a loop as if the other loops were very tightly tuned. For example, for the blender control system of Fig. 9-8, the ratio and mass balance controllers must be tuned first and be kept active while the flow and composition controllers are tuned.

An excellent method for tuning interacting loops is presented by Luyben (Reference 4), but it is based on frequency response techniques and, thus, outside the scope of this text.

9-5. Summary

This unit examined multivariable control systems and their tuning. The effect that loop interaction has on the response of feedback control systems was shown and two methods to deal with it were presented: Bristol's Relative Gain Matrix (RGM) for quantitatively determining the amount of interaction and for selecting the pairing of controlled and manipulated variables that minimizes the effect of interaction; and loop decoupling. The distillation column example showed that dynamic interaction, undetected by the relative gain matrix, must also be considered when pairing controlled and manipulated variables.

Exercises

9-1. Under what conditions does loop interaction take place? What are its effects? What two things can be done about it?

9-2. For any given loop in a multivariable (interacting) system, define the open-loop gain, the closed-loop gain, and the relative gain (interaction measure).

9-3. How is the relative gain matrix used to pair controlled and manipulated variables in an interacting control system? What makes it easy to determine the relative gains? What is the major shortcoming of the relative gain approach?

9-4. In a 2×2 control system the four relative gains are 0.5. Is there a best way to pair the variables to minimize the effect of interaction? By how much does the gain of a loop change when the other loop is closed? Is the interaction positive or negative?

9-5. Define positive and negative interaction. What is the range of values of the relative gain for each type of interaction?

9-6. The open-loop gains for the top and bottom compositions of a distillation column are the following:

	Reflux	Steam
Y_d	0.05	−0.02
X_b	−0.02	0.05

Calculate the relative gains and pair the compositions of the distillate (d) and bottoms (b) to the reflux and reboiler steam rates so that the effect of interaction is minimized.

9-7. The automated showers in the house of the 21st century will manipulate the hot and cold water flows to maintain constant water temperature and flow. In a typical design the system is to deliver 3 gallons per minute (gpm) of water at 110°F by mixing water at 170°F with water at 80°F. Determine the open-loop gains, the relative gains, and the preferred pairing for the two control loops. Hint:

The solution to this problem is identical to that of Example 9-2.

9-8. *Design a decoupler to maintain the temperature constant when the flow is changed in the shower control system of the preceding exercise. Dynamic effects can be neglected.*

References

1. Bristol, E. H., "On a Measure of Interaction for Multivariable Process Control," *IEEE Transactions on Automatic Control*, V. AC-11 (Jan. 1966), pp 133–134.
2. Cutler, C. R., and Ramaker, B. L., "DMC—A Computer Control Algorithm," AIChE 1979 Houston Meeting, Paper #516 (New York: AIChE, 1979).
3. Garcia, C. E., and Morari, M., "Internal Model Control, 2. Design Procedure for Multivariable Systems," *Industrial and Engineering Chemistry Process Design and Development*, V. 24 (1985), pp 472–484.
4. Luyben, W. L., *Process Modeling, Simulation, and Control for Chemical Engineers*, 2nd ed. (New York: McGraw-Hill, 1990).

Unit 10:
Adaptive and Self-Tuning Control

UNIT 10

Adaptive and Self-Tuning Control

One common characteristic of most process control systems is that they must deal with process characteristics that vary with process conditions and time, because the processes under control are nonlinear or time varying or both. This unit presents techniques for adapting the tuning parameters of the controller to the changing characteristics of the process.

Learning Objectives — When you have completed this unit you should:

A. Know when to apply adaptive and self-tuning control.

B. Understand the use of preset compensation, such as gain scheduling.

C. Be able to apply adaptive and self-tuning controllers based on pattern recognition or discrete model parameter estimation.

10-1. When Is Adaptive Control Needed?

Adaptive control is needed whenever process nonlinearities or time varying characteristics cause a significant change in the process dynamic parameters. Unit 3 explained that the dynamic behavior of a process can be characterized by the three parameters of a first-order plus dead time (FOPDT) model: the gain, the time constant, and the dead time (transportation lag or time delay). These parameters are usually functions of process operating conditions. Recall from Unit 4 that the controllability of a feedback loop, measured as the optimum performance of the controller, decreases with the ratio of the dead time to the time constant of the combined response of all the elements of the loop other than the controller.

As most feedback controllers are linear, once they are tuned at a given process operating condition, their performance will vary when the process operating conditions change. However, recalling that feedback control is usually a very robust strategy, small variations in process operating conditions would normally not change the process dynamic behavior enough to justify adaptive control techniques. Because of this robustness, the following apparently paradoxical statement can be made:

> Although almost all processes are nonlinear, very few processes require adaptive control.

Feedforward control would be more sensitive to changing process dynamic behavior were it not for the use of feedback trim on essentially all installations of feedforward and ratio control strategies. The presence of feedback trim makes these installations less sensitive to changing process operating conditions.

Even though most process control applications do not require adaptive control, the following examples illustrate common process nonlinearities and time dependences that may create the need for it.

Process Nonlinearities

Of the three process model parameters the one most likely to affect the performance of the loop is the gain. This is because the loop gain is directly proportional to the process gain, and, for the processes for which good control is important (temperature and composition), the loop gain is usually inversely proportional to process throughput (see section 3-6). A typical plot of process gain versus throughput is given in Fig. 10-1. This plot applies to the control of composition in a blender or of outlet temperature in a steam heater or furnace. The gain variation is even more pronounced in a heat exchanger in which the manipulated variable is the flow of a hot oil or coolant. This very common nonlinearity can be summarized in the following statement:

> For most temperature and composition control loops, the process gain decreases as the throughput—and, therefore, the position of the control valve—increases.

Many control schemes are expected to perform well at several throughput rates, as when a portion of the process is fed by two or more parallel trains, any number of which can be operating at any given time. This means that the throughput for the common portion of the process—and, consequently, its gain—will vary by factors of two and higher.

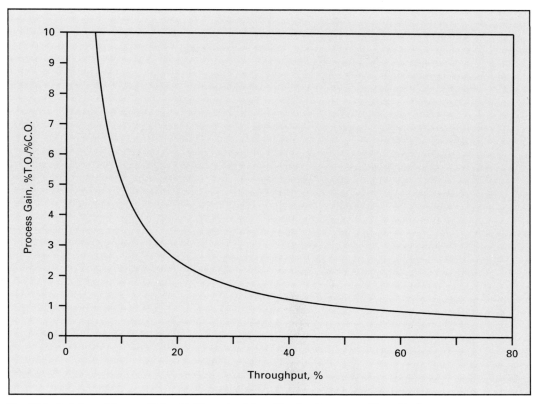

Fig. 10-1. Variation of Process Gain with Throughput for a Blender, Furnace, or Steam Heater.

Another common nonlinearity is the exponential dependence of reaction rates on temperature, which becomes important in batch reactors that are operated at different temperatures during the process. The dependence of reaction rate on composition also affects the process gain in batch reactors, especially if the reaction is carried to a high conversion; the effect is higher the higher the order of the reaction.

Finally, pH control loops present the highest degree of nonlinearity, as shown in the plot of pH versus the flow of the control stream in Fig. 10-2. As pH is a logarithmic function of the hydrogen ion concentration, when away from neutrality (pH of 7) the flow of the control stream must change by a factor of 10 to change the pH by each successive unit. This means that the controller must be able to change the flow by very small amounts when the pH is near 7 but by very large amounts when it is away from 7. Notice that in the pH loop,

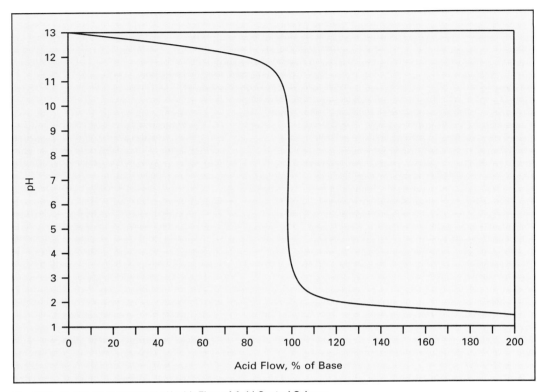

Fig. 10-2. Nonlinear Behavior of pH with Flow of Acid Control Scheme.

as before, the nonlinear behavior of the process results in a control loop with variable gain.

Process nonlinearities also affect the process time constants and dead time but usually to a lesser extent than they affect the gain. In particular, if the time constants and dead time were to remain proportional to each other as they vary (as they would in a blender when the throughput varies, for example), the controllability of the feedback loop would remain constant, since it is defined by the ratio of the effective dead time to the effective time constant of the loop. This means that, although the controller integral and derivative times would no longer match the speed of response of the process when the time parameters vary, for most loops the loop stability and damping of the response are not affected as much by the time parameters as they are by the variation of the gain.

Process Time Dependence

Besides nonlinear behavior, many process characteristics vary with time due to catalyst deactivation in reactors, fouling of heat exchanger tubes, coking of furnace tubes, and the like. In continuous processes, these variations occur over long periods of time (such as days or weeks) that are outside the time scale of the process response time. Nevertheless, they may require retuning of the controller during the cleanup or catalyst replacement cycles.

Other processes are sensitive to ambient conditions such as temperature or humidity (for example, large process air compressors and air-cooled condensers and exchangers). In such cases the cycles have periods of one day, riding on the annual cycle of the seasons. Yet another set of processes are affected by changes in product grade.

If the process characteristics change significantly with time, adaptive and self-tuning techniques are in order. Three adaptive control strategies—preset compensation, pattern recognition, and regression—will be presented next.

10-2. Preset Compensation

A common technique to maintain control loop performance in the face of changing process dynamics is to compensate for the variation of process parameters in a preset manner, based on knowledge of the process. The name "gain scheduling" has been applied to these techniques, indicating that the gain is the most important parameter to compensate. Indeed, the most common preset compensation practices deal with compensating for variations in process gain. These are the ones to be discussed in this section.

Because, as previously discussed, the inverse proportionality between process gain and throughput is the most common nonlinearity encountered in process control, preset compensation practice deals primarily with the variation of throughput. The three techniques presented here are the use of control valve characteristics, cascade to a ratio controller, and the use of gap or dead band controllers.

Valve Characteristics

As the control valve position is an indication of process throughput in most loops, designing the characteristic curve so that the increments in flow per unit change in valve position are proportional to the flow through the valve would exactly compensate for the decrease in process gain with throughput. Such a valve characteristic is the popular "equal percentage" characteristic, so called because the percentage increments in flow per unit change in valve position are equal (that is, the increments in flow are proportional to the current flow). The equal percentage valve characteristics are shown in Fig. 10-3.

When using equal percentage valve characteristics to compensate for the decrease in process gain with throughput, it is important to remember the following restrictions:

1. The valve must be designed so that the pressure drop across the valve remains constant over its range of operation. Otherwise, the actual installed characteristics would deviate from the equal percentage and aggravate the process gain variation problem when the valve is near fully opened. This phenomenon is indicated by the line of crosses in Fig. 10-3. For the valve to retain its equal

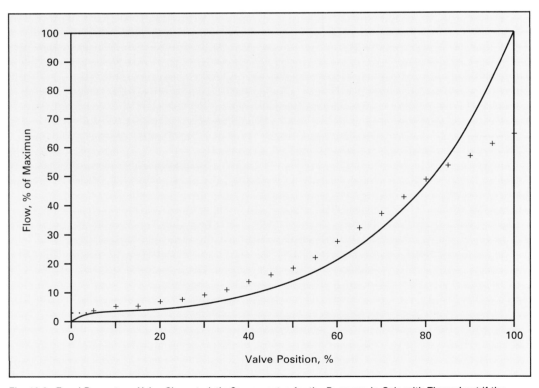

Fig. 10-3. Equal Percentage Valve Characteristic Compensates for the Decrease in Gain with Throughput if the Pressure Drop is Constant (Solid Line) but Not if the Pressure Drop Decreases as the Valve Opens (Crosses).

percentage characteristics, it must take up about 60% of the total flow-dependent pressure drop at the base capacity flow. For example, if the rest of the line in series with the valve takes up 5 psi of friction loss at design flow, the valve must take up $5(0.6/0.4) = 7.5$ psi at that flow.

2. If the temperature or composition controller is cascaded to a flow controller, the benefits of the equal percentage characteristics in the valve are lost to the temperature or composition loop. However, if the flow controller receives a differential pressure signal that is proportional to the square of the flow and does not extract the square root of this signal, the gain of the master controller would be compensated by the square function and, thus, increase with flow just as it would if it were connected to the equal percentage valve directly. Notice that if the flow controller receives a signal that is linear with flow, the output of the master controller will be linear with flow and its loop gain will decrease as the flow (throughput) increases.

3. The equal percentage characteristic curve does not produce zero flow at zero valve position. Therefore, the actual valve characteristic curve must deviate from the equal percentage characteristic curve in a region near the closed position, as it does in Fig. 10-3.

Keeping these restrictions in mind, equal percentage valves perform a natural compensation for the inverse proportionality between process gain and throughput.

Cascade to Ratio Control

Another way to compensate for the inverse proportionality between process gain and throughput is to ratio the manipulated flow to the throughput flow and have the temperature or composition controller set the ratio (cascade the feedback loop to a ratio controller). An example of such a scheme is shown in Fig. 10-4 for the control of composition out of a blender. The multiplication of the feedback controller output (the ratio) by the throughput flow makes the change in manipulated flow proportional to the throughput flow; thus, the feedback loop gain remains constant when the throughput flow changes.

Three examples of temperature control using this simple gain compensation scheme are shown in Fig. 10-5. In the three cases the fuel flow to a furnace, steam flow to a heater, and

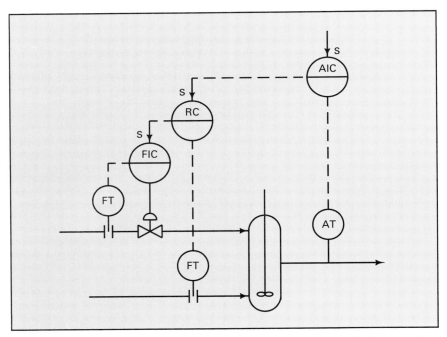

Fig. 10-4. Cascade to Ratio Controller Makes the Composition Loop Gain (AIC) Constant with Throughput.

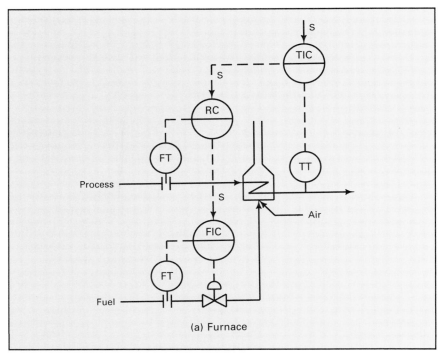

(a) Furnace

Fig. 10-5a. Cascade to Ratio Control of Temperature.

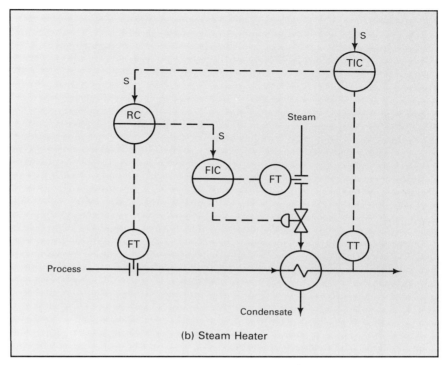

(b) Steam Heater

Fig. 10-5b.

hot oil heat rate to an exchanger are ratioed to the throughput flow. In the last example, the heat rate computation provides compensation for the temperature change of the hot oil—a feedforward compensation scheme.

Gap or Dead Band Controller

Special nonlinearities, such as the wide gain variation in the pH control system mentioned in the previous section, require special compensation strategies. One of the simplest and most commonly used pH control schemes is the one proposed by Shinskey (Reference 5), which uses two control valves in parallel and a gap controller. A schematic of the control scheme is shown in Fig. 10-6. In this scheme the pH controller (pHC) is proportional-only and directly manipulates the small control valve to adjust the flow of control stream (acid or base) to the neutralization tank. The output of the pH controller is fed to a valve-position controller (VPC) with a set point of 50% of range. The valve-position controller manipulates the position of a large valve in parallel with the small valve and with a capacity of about 20 times larger. The

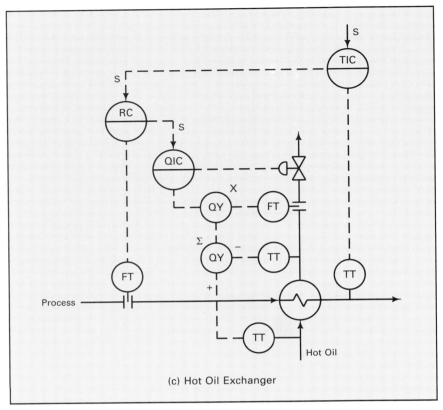

(c) Hot Oil Exchanger

Fig. 10-5c.

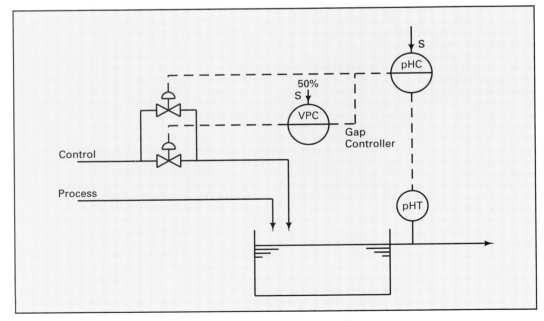

Fig. 10-6. pH Control Scheme Uses Two Control Valves and a Gap Controller.

gap or dead band on the valve-position controller keeps the large valve from moving while the small valve is making small adjustments in flow. When a large change in flow is required, the position of the small valve moves outside the dead band, and the VPC takes action to bring it back inside the dead band.

The VPC is proportional-integral and should operate so that the proportional part of the output does not jump when the valve position gets outside the band. The proper way to program it is to let it calculate its output all the time, changing it only if its input is outside the dead band.

The three techniques for compensation of process nonlinearity studied in this section are based on knowledge of the process and its behavior. They are only examples of what can be accomplished through proper design of the structure of the control system. Recall the general procedure for nonlinear feedforward controller design in Unit 8. One of the steps of that procedure was the selection of how the feedback trim was to enter into the feedforward compensation scheme. The cascade to ratio scheme just discussed is a special case of that general procedure, probably one of the simplest. By deciding that the feedback controller is to adjust the ratio, the effect of throughput rate on the process gain is compensated for. Similar compensation schemes can be arrived at with any nonlinear feedforward control system; the key step is the selection of the function of the feedback trim in the feedforward controller.

10-3. Adaptive Control by Pattern Recognition

With the use of microprocessors to carry out the PID feedback control functions, a natural development is the incorporation of "expert systems" to autotune and adapt the controller parameters to changing process characteristics. This section will briefly describe the pattern recognition controller marketed by The Foxboro Company as the EXACT™ controller, because this was the first controller in this class. The controller is based on an idea of Bristol (see Reference 2 for additional details). The overview presented here is based on a paper by Kraus and Myron (Reference 4).

Autotuning by pattern recognition is basically the programming of an expert system to automatically carry out the steps followed by an experienced control engineer or technician in tuning the controller. The principles behind this expert system are those used by Ziegler and Nichols in developing the quarter-decay ratio response formulas of Unit 2. The technique consists of recognizing a pattern in the closed-loop response of the loop, measuring its overshoot (or damping) and period of oscillation, and adjusting the controller parameters to match a specified response.

Recognizing the Response Pattern

The pattern recognition phase in the autotuning sequence starts when the error (difference between set point and controlled variable) exceeds a prespecified noise threshold. Such an error may be caused by a disturbance or a set point change. The program then searches for three peaks in the response, measures their amplitude and times, and calculates the overshoot, the damping (which is not independent of the overshoot), and the period of oscillation. A typical response is illustrated in Fig. 10-7. The definitions of overshoot and damping are as follows:

$$\text{Overshoot} = -E_2/E_1 \tag{10-1}$$

$$\text{Damping} = (E_3 - E_2)/(E_1 - E_2) \tag{10-2}$$

where E_1, E_2, and E_3 are the measured amplitude of the error at each of the three peaks. Notice that the error of the second

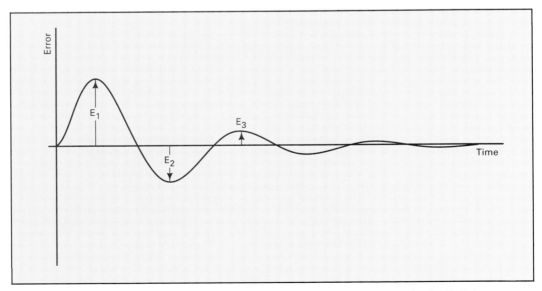

Fig. 10-7. Closed-Loop Response Showing the Peaks Used by the Pattern Recognition Adaptive Technique.

peak is assumed to be of the opposite sign to the other two, and, therefore, the differences indicated in the definition of the damping are actually sums.

When the response is not oscillatory, peaks 2 and 3 may not be detectable by the pattern recognition program. In such a case, they must be estimated for use in the tuning formulas.

Autotuning Formulas

The damping parameter and period of oscillation, coupled with the current controller parameters (gain, reset, and derivative times), define the tuning state of the closed loop much as the ultimate gain and period define it for the Ziegler-Nichols tuning formulas for quarter-decay ratio response (see section 2-6). In fact, the period determined by the pattern recognition program is very near the ultimate period of the loop, and the damping parameter defined by Eq. (10-2) is closely related to the quarter-decay response specification—the quarter-decay response produces a damping parameter of 0.5.

Formulas similar to the Ziegler-Nichols formulas are used to determine the integral and derivative times of the loop, subject to a user-specified "derivative factor" that adjusts the derivative relative to the value calculated by the tuning formulas. The gain is then adjusted to vary the damping in the desired direction, to match either a user-specified damping parameter or a predetermined default. An increase in gain increases the damping parameter, while a decrease in gain decreases it.

The controller parameters are calculated and reset to their new values only after the response has settled within the noise threshold band.

Autotuning Parameter Specifications

The autotuning algorithm is very easy to use because it requires a minimum of user specifications. It is also flexible because it allows additional optional specifications. The required specifications are:

- Initial controller gain, integral time, and derivative time.
- Noise band: the minimum magnitude of the error that triggers the pattern recognition program. This parameter

depends on the expected amplitude of the noise in the measured variable.
- Maximum wait time: the maximum time the algorithm will wait for the second peak in the response after detecting the first one. This parameter depends on the time scale of the process response.

Optional specifications include the maximum allowed damping and overshoot parameters, the derivative factor (which can be set to zero if a proportional-integral controller is desired), and the parameter change limit factor. This last parameter imposes a limit on the factor by which any of the controller parameters can be changed by the algorithm, based on the initial parameters.

Pretuning

The EXACT™ controller can automatically execute a pretuning procedure to determine the initial controller parameter values. The procedure, carried out with the controller in manual, consists of obtaining a step response of the process and first-order plus dead time model parameters, similar to those of Unit 3. The pretune algorithm automatically applies the step test on the controller output (of a magnitude specified by the user), waits for steady state, estimates the process parameters, calculates the initial controller parameters, and returns the controller output to its initial value.

Restrictions

The EXACT™ controller is a rule-based expert system with more than 200 rules, most of which deal with keeping the pattern recognition algorithm from being confused by peaks that are not caused by the controller tuning parameters. Nevertheless, it must be applied with much care, because in some situations the algorithm can be fooled. For example, oscillatory disturbances with a period of the same order of magnitude as that of the loop will tend to detune the controller, as the autotuning algorithm will think the oscillations are caused by too tight a controller tuning. Other situations such as loop interaction may also throw the autotuning off if not properly taken into account.

In summary, the EXACT™ controller shows the practicality of pattern recognition for autotuning feedback controllers. Many successful industrial applications have been reported. Although it is recommended that each application be carefully supervised by a control engineer during start-up and initial testing period, the algorithm should require little attention during normal operation, as it adapts the controller parameters to changing process characteristics.

10-4. Adaptive Control by Discrete Parameter Estimation

Like the pattern recognition adaptive controller, the discrete-model parameter estimation adaptive and autotuning controller naturally follows from the use of microprocessors for feedback control. Autotuning controllers based on the parameter estimation concept available commercially are the Leeds & Northrup Electromax V™ and the Turnbull Control Systems 600 Series™ controllers, among others.

Basically, the idea is to use linear recursive regression to estimate the parameters of a discrete linear model of the process from the sampled values of the controller output and controlled variable taken on-line. The discrete process parameters are then used in an adaptor to calculate the controller parameters, using formulas similar to those in Unit 6. An excellent discussion of this approach is in the text by Åström and Wittenmark (Reference 1), and all the mathematical details are in the text by Goodwin and Payne (Reference 3). The technique described in this section is the one originally developed by Touchstone and Corripio (Reference 7) and applied by Tompkins and Corripio (Reference 6) to autotune the temperature controllers on an industrial furnace using a PDP-8™ minicomputer.

Discrete Process Model

Unit 6 showed that a discrete second-order model of the process in the loop can be used to calculate the parameters of computer- and microprocessor-based PID control algorithms. It also showed that, if the model is reduced to first-order, the tuned algorithm reduces to a proportional-integral (PI) controller (the resulting derivative time is zero). The tuning formulas of Unit 6 reduce to the adjustment of a single parameter or control performance knob if the parameters of the discrete model can be independently estimated from process data. This is the basic idea behind the adaptive technique presented here.

The discrete model is given by the formula:

$$C_{n+1} = -A_1C_n - A_2C_{n-1} + B_0M_{n-N}$$
$$+ B_1M_{n-N-1} + B_2M_{n-N-2} \qquad (10\text{-}3)$$

where C_n and M_n are, respectively, the values of the controlled and manipulated variables at the nth sample time, N is the number of complete samples in the process dead time, and A_1, A_2, B_0, B_1, and B_2 are the parameters of the model.

There are several very desirable properties of the discrete model of Eq. (10-3):

1. This model can fit the response of most processes, both monotonic and oscillatory, with and without inverse response and with any ratio of dead time to sample time.
2. The parameters of the model can be estimated by linear multiple regression in a computer control installation, because the model equation is linear in the parameters and their coefficients are the known sampled values of the controlled variable and the controller output. Only the dead time parameter N must be estimated separately.
3. For a first-order process, the parameters A_2 and B_2 become zero, while, if the dead time is an exact number of samples, parameter B_2 is zero for the second-order process and B_1 is also zero for the first-order process.
4. Design of a controller for the model results in a PID algorithm with dead time compensation. The derivative time becomes zero for the first-order process, and a gain adjustment factor can be applied if dead time compensation is not used (see Unit 6).

In summary, the model fits the response of most processes, has parameters that can be estimated by a straightforward procedure, and results in the controller most commonly used in industry. How are the parameters estimated and how are they used to adapt the controller parameters?

Parameter Estimation

The estimation of the parameters of the discrete model can be done by straightforward multiple regression calculations. The calculations can be simple least squares regression if the measured process output (controlled variable C) is free of correlated measurement noise, but slightly more sophisticated calculations are required if this is not the case. The calculations can be carried out off-line after all the sampled values have been collected or recursively on-line (by updating the parameter estimates after each sample of the process variable and controller output).

Off-Line Least Squares Regression

Given k samples of the process variable C, k samples of the controller output M, and the necessary number of samples to account for the N samples of dead time, the least squares estimate of the vector of parameter estimates, $\mathbf{z}$, is simply obtained by solving the following system of linear equations:

$$(X'X)\mathbf{z} = X'\mathbf{y} \tag{10-4}$$

where $\mathbf{z}$ is a vector of the five discrete model parameters; X is a matrix of k rows, each of which is a vector of five elements consisting of the sampled values of the input and output, as follows:

$$\mathbf{z} = \begin{bmatrix} A_1 \\ A_2 \\ B_0 \\ B_1 \\ B_2 \end{bmatrix} \qquad X_n = [-C_n - C_{n-1}M_{n-N}M_{n-N-1}M_{n-N-2}]$$

Finally, $\mathbf{y}$ is a vector of the k sampled values of C_{n+1}.

Although the solution of Eq. (10-4) is straightforward with today's computers, there are several important requirements for the estimates of the process parameters to be good approximations of the actual process parameters, as follows:

1. During the data collection period the process variable C must be changing due to changes in the controller output M. The variations caused by M should be of greater magnitude than those caused by disturbances and measurement noise.

   The required variations in controller output can be applied directly to the controller output or to its set point, as shown in Fig. 10-8a. The signal can be as simple as a

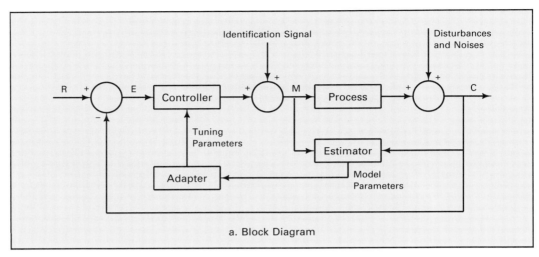

a. Block Diagram

Fig. 10-8a. Block Diagram of Adaptive Controller.

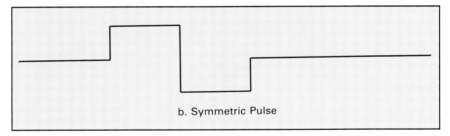

b. Symmetric Pulse

Fig. 10-8b.

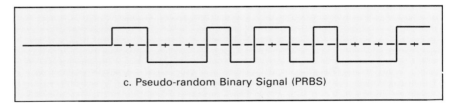

c. Pseudo-random Binary Signal (PRBS)

Fig. 10-8c.

symmetric pulse (Fig. 10-8b) or a pseudo-random binary sequence (Fig. 10-8c). The latter signal "excites" the process over a wider frequency range than the former. In either case, the data collection period should extend beyond the excitation period to allow the parameters to settle to average values.

2. The values of C and M used in the regression must be differences from an initial steady state. This can be

accomplished by subtracting the initial values of C and M from their respective sampled values. Alternatively, the values of C and M can be "differenced"; that is, they can be entered as differences of each sample minus the preceding sample.

3. The final values of C and M must match their initial values. This is not possible when a non-zero mean disturbance upsets the system during the data collection period. Differencing will get around this requirement. Another way to handle it is to add a parameter to Eq. (10-3) that will become an estimate of the mean value of the disturbance. The parameter vector **z** will then have a sixth element, and matrix X will have a sixth column consisting of ones [the coefficient of the new parameter in Eq. (10-3)].

4. Disturbances and measurement noise in process variable C must not be autocorrelated, because this would cause the estimates of the parameters to be biased. This problem can be handled through the estimation of a disturbance model. The method, known as maximum likelihood regression, is described in detail by Goodwin and Payne (Reference 3). Another method, instrumental variable regression, is more applicable to the recursive or on-line parameter estimation method.

All of the above restrictions apply also to the on-line or recursive parameter estimation method.

Recursive Parameter Estimation

The recursive method of estimating the process model parameters is applied on-line, with the calculations repeated each time a sample of the process variable is taken. The least squares estimate is improved incrementally after each sample by the following equation:

$$\mathbf{z}_{k+1} = \mathbf{z}_k + \mathbf{K}_{k+1}[C_{k+1} - \mathbf{x}'_{k+1}\mathbf{z}_k] \qquad (10\text{-}5)$$

where $\mathbf{z}_k$ is the vector of estimated model parameters after k samples, C_{k+1} is the process variable at sample $k + 1$, $\mathbf{x}'_{k+1}$ is defined by:

$$\mathbf{x}'_{k+1} = [-C_k - C_{k-1}M_{k-N}M_{k-N-1}M_{k-N-2}]$$

and the gain vector $\mathbf{K}_{k+1}$ is calculated as follows:

$$\mathbf{K}_{k+1} = P_k\mathbf{x}'_{k+1}/[\lambda + \mathbf{x}'_{k+1}P_k\mathbf{x}_{k+1}] \qquad (10\text{-}6)$$

The matrix P_k is the variance-covariance matrix. It contains information about past samples and is calculated recursively as follows:

$$P_{k+1} = P_k - K_{k+1}x'_{k+1}P_k/\lambda \qquad (10\text{-}7)$$

Parameter λ can be used to forget old samples. When λ is set to 1, as more samples are taken the elements of matrix P_k go to zero, and so does the gain K_k and, therefore, the effect that each sample has on the estimates of the parameters. To keep the estimator alive, λ is set to a positive value less than unity. The smaller the value of λ, the shorter the "memory" of the estimator in number of past samples.

To initialize the algorithm, initial estimates of the parameters, z_0, and an initial matrix P_0 are needed. The higher the initial value of the diagonal elements of P_0, the less confidence one has on the initial value of the corresponding element of z.

The matrix P_0 is best initialized as a diagonal matrix, that is, with all the elements off the diagonal set to zero. The diagonal elements can be started at sufficiently large values to cause the model parameters to change. If the diagonal elements are of the order of 100 or 1000, the parameters will change drastically for the first few samples. This is why it is better to skip these initial estimates in the adaptation of the controller parameters. If any of the diagonal elements of P_0 are set to zero, the corresponding parameter (element of z) will remain constant at its initial estimate.

Instrumental Variable Regression

To guard against biased estimates caused by correlated noise in the process variable, instrumental variable (IV) regression should be used instead of simple least squares. For instrumental variable regression, the gain K_{k+1} is calculated as follows:

$$K_{k+1} = P_k w_{k+1}/[\lambda + x'_{k+1}P_k w_{k+1}] \qquad (10\text{-}8)$$

where the vector w_{k+1} is given by:

$$w'_{k+1} = [-v_k - v_{k-1}M_{k-N}M_{k-N-1}M_{k-N-2}]$$

and v_k is the output of the model using the previously available estimates of the parameters:

$$v_k = \mathbf{w}'_k\mathbf{z}_k$$

The idea behind the instrumental variable approach is that the output of the model, v_k, should be well correlated with the true plant output but uncorrelated with the noise in the measurement of the process variable.

Variance of the Estimates

The matrix P_k is the variance-covariance matrix. Its diagonal elements, multiplied by the variance of the noise, yields the variance of the corresponding parameter estimate (element of $\mathbf{z}$). The calculation of the variance of the parameter estimates is difficult in the recursive mode, because it is not possible to calculate the variance of the noise. In the off-line method, the variance of the noise can be estimated as the variance of the residuals. At any rate, the "trace" of matrix P, that is, the sum of its diagonal elements, can serve as a good measure of the goodness of the fit.

Adapter

Unit 6 developed formulas for tuning PID controllers from continuous model parameters (process gain, time constants, and dead time). For autotuning and adapter controllers, similar formulas can be developed, using the same methods, from the discrete model parameters that are calculated by the estimator. The formulas for the parallel PID controller are as follows:

$$K_c = -\frac{(1 - q)(2A_2 + A_1)}{(B_0 + B_1 + B_2)[1 + N(1 - q)]}$$

$$T_I = -T(2A_2 + A_1)/(1 + A_1 + A_2) \qquad (10\text{-}9)$$

$$T_D = -A_2T/(2A_2 + A_1)$$

Notice that these formulas can be used to calculate the controller parameters from the estimated discrete model parameters. Parameter q is the control performance parameter, which can be adjusted to obtain tighter ($q \to 0$) or looser ($q \to 1$) control.

Autotuning versus Adaptive Control

The discrete model parameter estimation and adapter formulas can be used in both the autotuning and adaptive control modes. In the autotuning mode the program will be started at the desired time with $\lambda = 1$; the initial values of the model parameters will be calculated from the current controller parameters to avoid a bump; matrix P will be initialized; and the appropriate signal will be applied to the controller output or set point. The controller parameters will be adjusted until the parameter estimation gain dies out, at which time the autotuning procedure will be stopped. The autotuning procedure could then be repeated until the controller parameters do not change appreciably from the beginning to the end of a run.

In the adaptive mode the autotuning program is allowed to run all the time, taking advantage of process disturbances and normal set point changes. The initialization need be performed only once, and estimation parameter λ is set to a value less than unity to keep the estimator alive.

A successful application of the instrumental variable autotuning method to a set of steam cracking furnaces was reported by Tompkins and Corripio (Reference 6). The following example will illustrate the use of the procedure and provide a benchmark against which to test autotuning programs.

Example 10-1, Process Identification by Least Squares Regression: To test the efficiency of the least squares parameter estimation technique, it is applied to a known linear second-order discrete model with the following parameters:

Gain: 2 %/%   Time constants: 1.0 and 0.5 min

Sample time: 0.2 min

The dead time and lead term are zero. The discrete second-order model for the parameters given above is:

$$C_{n+1} = 1.48905\ C_n - 0.54881\ C_{n-1} + 0.065717\ M_n$$

$$+ 0.0538046\ M_{n-1} + U_{n+1}$$

where U is a random signal varying between -0.05% and $+0.05\%$, which is added to simulate measurement noise. The mean value of this noise signal is approximately zero.

The process identification is carried out by applying a pseudo-random binary signal (PRBS) with amplitude of -1% to 1% for the input M_n. The signal is allowed to change every 4 samples (0.8 min) and is run for 120 samples. Data on C_n and M_n are collected for 20 more samples (a total of 141 samples, including the initial value). A plot of the input and output data is given in Fig. 10-9.

The response data are input to an off-line least squares identification program and to a recursive estimator. The initial variance/covariance matrix (P) for the recursive estimator is a diagonal matrix with all the diagonal terms set to 1000, and the forgetting factor λ is set to 1.0 (no forgetting of past

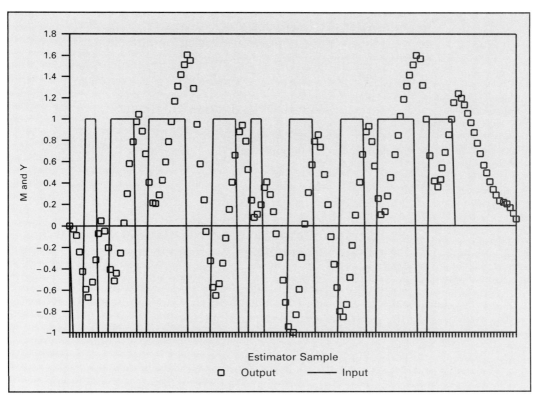

Fig. 10-9. Input and Output Data Used for Parameter Estimation in Example 10-1.

samples). The parameters of the following second-order discrete model are estimated:

$$C_{n+1} = -A_1 C_n - A_2 C_{n-1} + B_0 M_{n-N}$$

$$+ B_1 M_{n-N-1} + B_2 M_{n-N-2} + D$$

With $N = 0$, the results are summarized below:

Parameter	True Value	Recursive Estimate	Off-Line Estimate	Standard Deviation
A_1	−1.48905	−1.50320	−1.50672	0.01929
A_2	0.54881	0.56066	0.56401	0.01844
B_0	0.06571	0.06263	0.06270	0.00201
B_1	0.05380	0.05467	0.05446	0.00275
B_2	0	−0.00124	−0.00177	0.00352
D	0	0.00049	0.00055	0.00152

Parameter D is added to the model to account for the mean value of the noise or for a sustained disturbance. All of the parameter estimates are within two standard deviations (95% confidence limits) of the true values, and the standard deviations of the estimates are within 10% of their estimated values. More importantly, the tuning parameters calculated from the estimated model parameters are practically the same as those calculated from the true parameters, as shown below:

Parallel PID Tuning Parameters

Parameter	From True Parameters	From Recursive Estimates	From Off-Line Estimates
Prop. gain, %/%	3.27	3.29	3.28
Reset time, min	1.31	1.33	1.32
Deriv. time, min	0.28	0.29	0.30

where the proportional gains are calculated with $q = 0$; that is, they are the maximum gains recommended by Eqs. (10-9). There is no difference between the tuning parameters derived from the estimated parameters or the real parameters; therefore, an autotuner based on the least squares estimates would produce excellent results.

Figure 10-10 shows a plot of the response of the second-order process (with the real parameters) to a set point change. The controller tuning parameters are those derived from the recursive least squares estimates of the model parameters. As would be expected, the response is excellent.

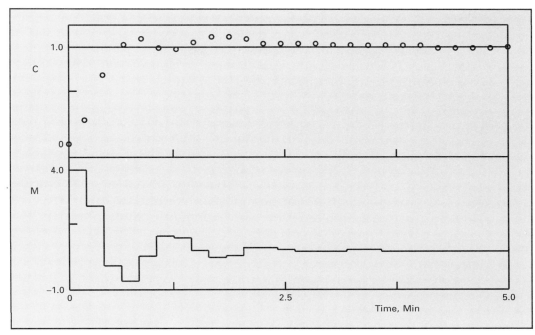

Fig. 10-10. Response of Autotuned Controller of Example 10-1 to a Change in Set Point.

The preceding example demonstrates how successful least squares regression can be for autotuning controllers for a simple process. If the process had dead time, the results would be just as good if the true value of the dead time parameter, N, were used in the estimation. The presence of a lead term in the process transfer function (inverse or overshoot response) does not present any difficulty to the performance of the estimator or its accuracy. However, if the noise term (U) were autocorrelated, the instrumental variable estimation procedure should be used.

10-5. Summary

This unit has presented techniques for adaptive and autotuning control. Although most process controllers do not require adaptive control, it is important to recognize those situations where process nonlinearities may adversely affect the performance of the control system. In many cases the nonlinearities can be compensated by proper selection of the control valve characteristics or by proper design of the feedforward control system. Pattern recognition and discrete model regression are excellent techniques for adaptive and autotuning control.

Exercises

10-1. What characteristic of the process will make it worthwhile to apply adaptive control? Do most control loops require adaptive control?

10-2. Which of the process parameters is most likely to vary and thus affect the performance of the control loop? Give an example.

10-3. How can the control valve characteristic be selected to compensate for process gain variations? Cite the restrictions for the valve characteristic to properly compensate for gain variations.

10-4. How does the cascade of a feedback controller to a ratio controller compensate for process gain variation?

10-5. Why is a gap controller useful for controlling pH?

10-6. Briefly describe the adaptive and autotuning techniques based on pattern recognition.

10-7. Why is a second-order discrete model useful to identify the dynamic response of most processes? Why is it easy to estimate its parameters?

10-8. Cite the requirements for the least squares estimation of the parameters of the discrete process model.

10-9. Why is it desirable to estimate the process parameters recursively on-line? Describe how such a technique can be used for both adaptive and autotuning control.

10-10. What is the meaning of the diagonal elements of the variance-covariance matrix P_k? How can they be initialized to keep a parameter from varying during the estimation calculations?

References

1. Åström, K. J., and Wittenmark, Björn, Computer Controlled Systems (Englewood Cliffs, NJ: Prentice-Hall, 1984), chs. 13 and 14.
2. Bristol, E. H., ''Pattern Recognition: An Alternative to Parameter Estimation in Adaptive Control,'' Automatica, V. 13 (Mar. 1977), pp 197–202.

3. Goodwin, G. C., and Payne, R. L., *Dynamic System Identification: Experiment Design and Data Analysis* (New York: Academic Press, 1977).

4. Kraus, T. W., and Myron, T. J., "Self-Tuning PID Controller Uses Pattern Recognition Approach," *Control Engineering* (June 1984), pp 106–111.

5. Shinskey, F. G., *Process Control Systems*, 3rd ed. (New York: McGraw-Hill, 1989).

6. Tompkins, P. M., and Corripio, A. B., "Industrial Application of a Self-Tuning Feedback Control Algorithm," *ISA Transactions*, V. 20, No. 2 (1981), pp 3–10.

7. Touchstone, A. T., and Corripio, A. B., "Adaptive Control through Instrumental Variable Estimation of Discrete Model Parameters," *Proceedings of ISA/77* (Research Triangle Park, NC: ISA, 1977), pp 57–64.

Appendix A:
Suggested Reading
and Study Materials

APPENDIX A

Suggested Reading and Study Materials

Independent Learning Modules

Murrill, P. W., *Fundamentals of Process Control Theory* (Research Triangle Park, NC: ISA, 1981).

Shinskey, F. G., *Controlling Multivariable Processes* (Research Triangle Park, NC: ISA, 1981)

Textbooks (selected titles)

Åström, K. J., and Hagglund, T., *Automatic Tuning of PID Controllers* (Research Triangle Park, NC: ISA, 1988).

Deshpande, P. B., and Ash, R. H., *Computer Process Control*, 2nd ed. (Research Triangle Park, NC: ISA, 1989).

McAvoy, T. J., *Interaction Analysis: Principles and Applications* (Research Triangle Park, NC: ISA, 1983).

McMillan, G. K., *Tuning and Control Loop Performance*, 2nd ed. (Research Triangle Park, NC: ISA, 1990).

Shinskey, F. G., *Process Control Systems*, 3rd ed. (New York, NY: McGraw-Hill, 1989).

Seborg, D. E., Edgar, T. F., and Mellichamp, D. A., *Process Dynamics and Control* (New York, NY: Wiley, 1989).

Smith, C. A., and Corripio, A. B., *Principles and Practice of Automatic Process Control* (New York, NY: Wiley, 1985).

Smith, C. L., *Digital Computer Process Control* (Scranton, PA: International Textbook Publishers, 1972).

Technical Magazines and Journals (selected titles)

- *AIChE Journal*, published by the American Institute of Chemical Engineers, New York.
- *Automatica*, published by Pergamon Press, New York.
- *Control Engineering*, published by Dun-Donnelly Pub. Corp., New York.
- *Industrial and Engineering Chemistry Research*, published by the American Chemical Society, Washington, D.C.
- *ISA Transactions*, published by the Instrument Society of America.
- *InTech*, published by the Instrument Society of America.
- *Instruments and Control Systems*, published by Chilton, Philadelphia.

Appendix B:
BASIC Program Listing for Discrete Loop Tuning

APPENDIX B

BASIC Program Listing for Discrete Loop Tuning

DISCLOOP

```
100 REM       Simulation of Sampled-Data Control Loop with Second Order Plant
110 REM
120 REM                       Default Parameters
130 REM
140 MP = 12 : ULENGTH%=1000
150 DIM TSM(ULENGTH%), YS(ULENGTH%), US(ULENGTH%), USTACK(ULENGTH%)
160 W = 10
170 Q$ = CHR$(34)
180 READ TMAX, GAIN, TAU1, TAU2, TAU3, DT, TS, NM, DTC%
190 DATA 5, 1, 1, 0, 0, 0, 0.1, 0, 0
200 READ KW, TAW1, TAW2, TAW3, RK
210 DATA 0, 0, 0, 0, 1
220 READ KC, TI, TD, ALPHA, Q, ULOW, UHIGH
230 DATA 1., 1, 0, 0.1, 0, -10, 10
240 CTYPE$="Series" : DT$="DY" : DTYPE$="Derivative on measurement"
250 PT$ = "PE" : PTYPE$ = "Proportional on error"
260 NSAMP = INT(TMAX/TS + .5) : GOSUB 900 : GOSUB 1320
270 COLOR 14,0 : CLS
280 PRINT "Simulation of Sampled-Data Control Loop with Second-Order Plant"
290 PRINT
300 PRINT "The plant transfer function consists of"
310 PRINT
320 PRINT ,"Numerator:     (GAIN)  (LEAD 'TAU3')  (DEAD TIME 'DT')"
330 PRINT
340 PRINT ,"Denominator:    (LAG 'TAU1')  (LAG 'TAU2')"
350 PRINT
360 PRINT "The disturbance model is the same, but without the dead time."
370 PRINT
380 PRINT "The program will accept the continuous model parameters and"
390 PRINT "compute the parameters of the discrete model given by:"
400 PRINT
410 PRINT "Y(T)= -A1*Y(T-1) - A2*Y(T-2) + BO*U(T-N-1) + B1*U(T-N-2)";
420 PRINT " + B2*U(T-N-3)"
430 PRINT : PRINT "where N is Int(DT/TS) and TS is  the sample interval."
440 COLOR 7,0
450 GOSUB 640
460 REM
470 CLS : PRINT "Main Menu:" : PRINT
480 REM
490 PRINT ,"Run time and sample time specification"
500 PRINT ,"Process model parameter specification"
510 PRINT ,"Disturbance model/set point change"
520 PRINT ,"Controller specification and tuning"
530 PRINT : PRINT ,"Loop response calculation"
540 PRINT ,"Output results"
550 PRINT "Any other character to stop program." : PRINT
560 OPT$ = "RPDCLO": GOSUB 591
570 ON OPT GOSUB 660, 820, 1240, 1630, 2500, 3250
580 PRINT ,,"Oops! To resume, enter the CONT command.": END
590 GOTO 460
591 REM          Convert option character to number
592 PRINT : PRINT "Which option do you want? (Capitalized letter): ";
593 GOSUB 600: PRINT A$: FOR OPT = 1 to LEN( OPT$ )
594 IF MID$( OPT$, OPT, 1 ) = CHR$( ASC( A$ ) AND 223 ) THEN RETURN
595 NEXT OPT: OPT = 0: RETURN
```

```
600 REM
610 REM            Pause routine
620 REM
630 A$=INKEY$: IF A$="" THEN 630 ELSE RETURN
640 KEY OFF: LOCATE 25,50 : COLOR 14: PRINT "Hit any key to continue"
650 GOSUB 600: COLOR 7,0 : RETURN
660 REM
670 CLS : PRINT "Specify Run Time and Sample Time:" : PRINT
680 REM
690 PRINT, "Run Time   TMAX: ";TMAX: PRINT , "Sample time  TS: ";TS
700 PRINT : PRINT "CAUTION: Run Time must not exceed ";ULENGTH%;" samples"
710 PRINT : OPT$ = "RS": GOSUB 591
720 ON OPT GOTO 740, 770
730 GOTO 460
740 INPUT "Enter run time";TMAX
750 IF TMAX <= 0 THEN TMAX = 10*TAU1 + DT
760 GOTO 800
770 INPUT "Enter sample time";TS
780 IF TS <= 0 THEN TS = .1*TAU1
790 GOSUB 900 : GOSUB 1320
800 NSAMP = INT(TMAX/TS + .5) : GOTO 660
810 REM
820 CLS : PRINT "Process Model Parameters:"
830 REM
860 GOSUB 900 : GOTO 1110
870 REM
880 REM            Calculation of the Model Parameters
890 REM
900 RATIO= DT/TS : N= INT(RATIO) : MT = 1 - (RATIO-N)
910 IF TAU1<=0 THEN TAU1!
920 IF ABS( TAU2/TAU1 - 1) <= .01 THEN 1000
930     A= EXP(-TS/TAU1) : IF TAU2>0 THEN B=EXP(-TS/TAU2)
940     A1= -A - B : A2 = A*B : C1= (TAU1-TAU3)/(TAU1-TAU2)*A^MT
950                             C2= (TAU2-TAU3)/(TAU1-TAU2)*B^MT
960     B0= GAIN*(1 - C1 + C2 )
970     B1= GAIN*(A1 + C1*(1+B) - C2*(1+A) )
980     B2= GAIN*(A2 - C1*B + C2*A )
990       GOTO 1050
1000              A= EXP(-TS/TAU1)           Identical time constants
1010              A1= -2*A : A2= A^2 : C= (TAU1-TAU3)/TAU1^2*TS
1020              B0= GAIN*( 1 - A^MT*( 1 + C*MT ) )
1030              B1= GAIN*( -2*A + A^MT*( 1 + C*MT + A*( 1 + C*(MT-1) ) ) )
1040              B2= GAIN*( A^2 - A^(MT+1)*( 1 + C*(MT-1) ) )
1050 REM
1060 PRINT :PRINT "Discrete process model parameters:"
1070   PRINT "    B0=";B0;"     B1=";B1;"     B2=";B2
1080   PRINT "    A1=";A1;"    A2=";A2: PRINT "    Dead time: N=";N;"
                                                               M=";MT
1090 RETURN
1100 REM
1110 PRINT : PRINT "Select a parameter to change:"
1115 PRINT, "Gain              : ";GAIN
1120 PRINT ,"First lag  TAU1: ";TAU1
1125 PRINT ,"Second lag TAU2: ";TAU2
1130 PRINT ,"Lead term  TAU3: ";TAU3
1140 PRINT ,"Dead time    DT: ";DT
1145 PRINT : PRINT "Any other letter to return to main menu."
1150 OPT$= "GFSLD": GOSUB 591
1160 ON OPT GOTO 1180, 1190, 1200, 1210, 1220
1170 GOTO 460
1180 PRINT : INPUT "Enter GAIN";GAIN : GOTO 820
1190 PRINT : INPUT "Enter TAU1";TAU1 : GOTO 820
1200 PRINT : INPUT "Enter TAU2";TAU2 : GOTO 820
1210 PRINT : INPUT "Enter TAU3";TAU3 : GOTO 820
1220 PRINT : INPUT "Enter DT" ;DT" : GOTO 820
```

```
1230 REM
1240 CLS : PRINT "Disturbance Model Parameters / Set point input:"
1250 REM
1280 GOSUB 1320 : GOTO 1510
1290 REM
1300 REM            Calculation of the disturbance model parameters
1310 REM
1320 IF TAW1>0 THEN 1340                        'Step response if TAW1=0
1330    AW1=0 : AW2=0 : BW0=KW : BW1 = 0 : GOTO 1450
1340 IF ABS( TAW2/TAW1 - 1 ) <= .01 THEN 1410
1350    A= EXP(-TS/TAW1) : B=0 : IF TAW2>0 THEN B=EXP(-TS/TAW2)
1360    AW1= -A - B : AW2 = A*B : C1= (TAW1-TAW3)/(TAW1-TAW2)*A
1370                              C2= (TAW2-TAW3)/(TAW1-TAW2)*B
1380    BW0= KW*(1 - C1 + C2 )
1390    BW1= KW*(AW1 + C1*(1+B) - C2*(1+A) )
1400       GOTO 1450
1410             A= EXP(-TS/TAW1)             'Identical time constants
1420             AW1= -2*A : AW2= A^2 : C= (TAW1-TAW3)/TAW1^2*TS
1430             BW0= KW*( 1 - A*( 1 + C ) )
1440             BW1= KW*( -2*A + A*( 1 + C + A ) )
1450 REM
1460 PRINT :PRINT "Discrete disturbance model parameters:"
1470    PRINT ,"BW0=";BW0;"       BW1=";BW1
1480    PRINT ,"AW1=";AW1;"       AW2=";AW2
1490 RETURN
1500 REM
1510 PRINT : PRINT "Select a parameter to change:": PRINT
1515 PRINT ,"Gain on disturbance KW: ";KW
1520 PRINT ,"First lag           TAW1: ";TAW1
1525 PRINT ,"Second lag          TAW2: ";TAW2
1530 PRINT ,"Lead term           TAW3: ";TAW3
1540 PRINT ,"Change in set point RK: ";RK
1545 PRINT: PRINT "Any other letter to return to main menu."
1550 OPT$ = "GFSLC": GOSUB 591
1560 ON OPT GOTO 1580, 1590, 1600, 1610, 1620
1570 GOTO 460
1580 PRINT : INPUT "Enter gain (zero for no disturbance)";KW : GOTO 1240
1590 PRINT : INPUT "Enter TAU1 (zero for step change)";TAW1 : GOTO 1240
1600 PRINT : INPUT "Enter TAU2 (ignored if TAU1=0)";TAW2 : GOTO 1240
1610 PRINT : INPUT "Enter TAU3 (ignored if TAU1=0)";TAW3 : GOTO 1240
1620 PRINT : INPUT "Enter set point change";RK : GOTO 1240
1630 REM
1640 REM               Specify and Tune Sampled Data Controller
1650 REM
1660 CLS : PRINT CTYPE$;" PID Algorithm, ";DTYPE$;", ";PTYPE$
1670 PRINT : PRINT "Controller parameters: "
1680 PRINT "Kc:";KC;"     Ti:";TI"    Td:";TD
1710 GOSUB 1730 : GOTO 1770
1720 REM
1730 GAMMA = ALPHA*TD/(TS + ALPHA*TD)
1740 IF CTYPE$ = "Parallel" THEN TDOT = TD/(TS + ALPHA*TD) : GOTO 1760
1750   LEAD = (ALPHA + 1)*TD/(TS + ALPHA*TD)    'Series net lead
1760 RETURN
1770 PRINT : PRINT "Discrete parameters:" : PRINT
1780 PRINT "Derivative filter parameter, GAMMA:";GAMMA;"      ";
1790 IF CTYPE$ = "Parallel" THEN PRINT "Parallel TD/TS:";TDOT : GOTO 1810
1800   PRINT "Series lead term:";LEAD
1810 REM
1820 PRINT : PRINT "Select controller parameter to change:": PRINT
1830 PRINT "     Series or parallel controller         : ";CTYPE$
1840 PRINT "     Derivative on error or measurement    : ";DTYPE$
1850 PRINT "     Proportional on error or measurement : ";PTYPE$
1860 PRINT "     Filter parameter for derivative term : ";ALPHA
1870 PRINT "     Compensation for dead time            : ";DTC%;
1875 IF DTC%<>0 THEN PRINT " (";NM;" samples)": ELSE PRINT
```

```
1880 PRINT "      Limits on controller output                : ";ULOW;" to ;UHIGH
1890 PRINT : PRINT "   Tune the controller"
1900 PRINT : PRINT "Any other character to return to main menu."
1910 OPT$ = "SDPFCLT": GOSUB 591
1920 ON OPT GOTO 1940, 1970, 2020, 2060, 2070, 2110, 2130
1930 GOTO 460
1940 PRINT : INPUT "Series (S) or parallel (P)";TYP$
1950   IF TYP$ = "p" OR TYP$ = "P" THEN CTYPE$="Parallel" ELSE CTYPE$="Series"
1960   GOTO 1630
1970 IF CTYPE$="Series" THEN PRINT "Series controller is always DY" : GOTO 1630
1980 PRINT : INPUT "Derivative on error (DE) or measurement (DY)";DT$
1990   IF DT$="de" OR DT$="DE" THEN 2010
2000   DT$="DY" : DTYPE$ = "Derivative on measurement" : GOTO 1630
2010     DT$="DE" : DTYPE$ = "Derivative on error" : GOTO 1630
2020 PRINT : INPUT "Proportional on error (PE) or measurement (PY)";PT$
2030   IF PT$="py" OR PT$="PY" THEN 2050
2040   PT$="PE" : PTYPE$ = "Proportional on error" : GOTO 1630
2050     PT$="PY" : PTYPE$ = "Proportional on measurement" : GOTO 1630
2060 PRINT : INPUT "Derivative filter parameter, ALPHA:";ALPHA : GOTO 1630
2070 PRINT : INPUT "Dead time compensation (0=No; 1=Yes)";DTC%
2080   IF DTC%<>0 THEN INPUT "Samples of dead time compensation"; NM
2090   IF NM < 0THEN NM=0
2100   GOSUB 2140: GOTO 1630
2110 PRINT : INPUT "Controller output lower limit, ULOW";ULOW
2120   INPUT "Controller output upper limit, UHIGH";UHIGH : GOTO 1630
2130 GOSUB 2140: GOTO 1630
2140 REM
2150 CLS : PRINT CTYPE$;" Controller Tuning:" : PRINT
2160 IF TAU1 < TAU2 THEN 2190
2170   A = EXP(-TS/TAU1) : B = 0 : IF TAU2 > 0 THEN B=EXP(-TS/TAU2)
2180   GOTO 2200
2190     A=EXP(-TS/TAU2) : B=EXP(-TS/TAU1)
2200 IF CTYPE$="Parallel" THEN 2240
2210   KC=(1-Q)*A/(GAIN*(1-A))
2220   TI=TS*A/(1-A)
2230   TD=TS*B/(1-B) : GOTO 2270
2240     KC=(A-2*A*B+B)*(1-Q)/(GAIN*(1-A)*(1-B))
2250     TI=TS*(A-2*A*B+B)*(1-Q)/((1-A)*(1-B))
2260     TD=TS*A*B/(A-2*A*B+B)
2270 IF DTC%=0 THEN KC=KC/(1+NM*(1-Q))
2290 CLS
2300 PRINT : PRINT "Select tuning parameter to change:"
2310 PRINT : PRINT ,"Proportional gain         Kc: ";KC
2320 PRINT ,"Integral (reset) time     Ti: ";TI
2330 PRINT ,"Derivative (rate) time    Td: ";TD
2340 PRINT ,"Tuning (Dahlin) parameter  q: ";Q
2345 PRINT ,"Model dead time           NM: ";NM
2350 PRINT "Any other letter to return to previous menu."
2360 OPT$ = "PIDTM": GOSUB 591
2370 ON OPT GOTO 2390, 2400, 2420, 2440, 2462
2380 RETURN
2390 PRINT : INPUT "Controller gain";KC : PRINT : GOTO 2290
2400 PRINT : INPUT "Integral or reset time";TI : PRINT : IF TI<=0 THEN TI=TS
2410   GOTO 2290
2420 PRINT : INPUT "Derivative or rate time";TD : PRINT : IF TD<0 THEN TD=0
2430   GOTO 2290
2440 PRINT : INPUT "Dahlin tuning parameter, q=exp(-Lambda/ts)"; Q
2450   IF Q<0 OR Q>=1 THEN Q=0
2460   GOTO 2140
2462 PRINT : INPUT "Number of samples in model dead time"; NM
2464   IF NM<0 THEN NM =0
2466   GOTO 2140
2470 REM
2480 REM                Calculation of Loop Response
2490 REM
```

```
2500 PRINT : PRINT "Closed-loop response for ";NSAMP;" samples"
2510 PRINT : PRINT "Un momento por favor..."
2520 REM
2530 REM                              Initialize variables
2540 REM
2550 CKM1=0: CK=0: UKMNM2=0: UKMNM1=0: UK=0 : IAE = 0
2560 WKM1=0: WK=0: YKM1=0 : YK=0 : BK=0 : XK=0: VKM1=0: VK=0: DUDK=0
2570 UIN=0 : GOSUB 3050                        'Initialize delay stack
2580 GOSUB 2870                                'Calculate initial controller output
2590 TSM(0)=0 : YS(0) = YK: US(0)=UK
2600 CLS : LOCATE 12,30 : PRINT "Calculating sample"
2610 LOCATE 14,35 : PRINT "IAE:"
2620 REM
2630 REM                              Calculation Loop
2640 REM
2650 FOR ISAMP=1 TO NSAMP: GOSUB 2700
2660 LOCATE 12,50 : PRINT ISAMP;" of ";NSAMP
2670 LOCATE 14,40 : IAE = IAE + TS*ABS(RK-YK) : PRINT IAE
2680 TSM(ISAMP)=ISAMP*TS : YS(ISAMP) = YK : US(ISAMP)=UK : NEXT ISAMP
2690 GOSUB 640 : GOTO 460
2700 REM
2710 REM               Calculation of sampled response
2720 REM
2730 CKM2=CKM1: CKM1:=CK
2740 UDELAY%=N+1 : GOSUB 3190                          'Retrieve delayed output
2750 UKMNM3=UKMNM2 : UKMNM2 = UKMNM1 : UKMNM1=UOUT
2760 CK= -A1*CKM1 - A2*CKM2 + B0*UKMNM1 + B1*UKMNM2 + B2*UKMNM3
2770 GOSUB 2810 : YKM1=YK : YK = CK + WK         'Calculate wk and yk
2780 GOSUB 2870                                  'Calculate controller output
2790 RETURN
2800 REM
2810 REM                         Calculate disturbance model
2820 REM
2830 WKM2=WKM1 : WKM1 = WK
2840 IF ISAMP<=1 THEN WK = BW0 : RETURN
2850 WK = -AW1*WKM1 -AW2*WKM2 + BW0 + BW1 : RETURN
2860 REM
2870 REM                         Calculate controller output
2880 REM
2890 IF CTYPE$="Parallel" THEN=-YK : GOTO 2910
2900 BKM1=BK : BK = GAMMA*BKM1 - (1-GAMMA)*YK - LEAD*(YK - YKM1)
2910 EK = RK + BK : DUIK = (TS/TI)*EK                   'Integral term
2920 XKM1 = XK : IF PT$="PE" THEN XK=EK ELSE XK=BK
2930 DUPK = XK - XKM1                          'Proportional term
2940 IF CTYPE$="Parallel" THEN 2950 ELSE 2970
2950    VKM2=VM1 : VKM1=VK : IF DT$="DE" THEN VK=EK ELSE VK=-YK
2960    DUDKM1=DUDK : DUDK = GAMMA*DUDKM1 + TDOT*(VK - 2*VKM1 + VKM2)
2970 DUK = KC*(DUPK + DUIK + DUDK)                'Output increment
2980 UKM1=UK : UK = UKM1 + DUK
2990 IF DTC%<>0 THEN 3000 ELSE 3020               'Dead Time Compensation
3000    UDELAY%=NM+1 : GOSUB 3190                 'Retrieve delayed output
3010    UK = UK + (1-Q)*(UOUT - UKM1)
3020 IF UK < ULOW THEN UK=ULOW ELSE IF UK > UHIGH THEN UK = UHIGH
3030 UIN = UK : GOSUB 3120                         'Store in stack
3040 RETURN
3050 REM
3060 REM          Initialize delay stack
3070 REM
3080 FOR I=1 TO ULENGTH% : USTACK(I) = UIN : NEXT I
3090 UINDEX%=1
3100 RETURN
3110 REM
3120 REM                    Store value in stack
3130 REM
3140 USTACK(UINDEX%) = UIN
```

```
3150 UINDEX% = UINDEX% + 1
3160 IF UINDEX%>ULENGTH% THEN UINDEX% = 1
3170 RETURN
3180 REM
3190 REM                                Retrieve value from stack
3200 REM
3210 ULOC% = UINDEX%-1 : IF UDELAY%>1 THEN ULOC% = UNINDEX% - UDELAY%
3220 IF ULOC%<=0 THEN ULOC%=ULOC% + ULENGTH%
3230 UOUT = USTACK(ULOC%)
3240 RETURN
3250 REM
3260 CLS : PRINT : PRINT "Output of Results"
3270 REM
3280 PRINT : PRINT "Options:
3290 PRINT : PRINT ,"Table of input and output responses"
3300 PRINT ,"Graph of input and output responses"
3310 PRINT ,"Store results for input to spreadsheet"
3320 PRINT ,"Print to online printer"
3330 PRINT : PRINT "Any other letter to return to main menu."
3340 OPT$ = "TGSP": GOSUB 591
3350 ON OPT GOTO 3400, 3510, 3620, 3850
3360 GOTO 460
3370 REM
3380 REM                Results Table to Screen
3390 REM
3400 CLS : PRINT USING "\        \";" Time ","    Y   ","    U   ",
3410 PRINT USING "\        \";"  Time ","      Y  ","      U  ",
3420 PRINT USING "\        \";"   Time","       Y  ","       U  ": PRINT
3430 FOR I=0 TO NSAMP STEP 3
3440    PRINT USING "##.#### ";TSM(I), YS(I), US(I),: PRINT USING "!";":",
3450    PRINT USING "##.#### ";TSM(I+1), YS(I+1), US(I+1),: PRINT USING "!";":",
3460    PRINT USING "##.#### ";TSM(I+2), YS(I+2), US(I+2)
3470    IF I>0 AND I=57*INT(I/57) THEN GOSUB 640
3480    NEXT I
3490 PRINT : PRINT "IAE:";IAE
3500 GOSUB 610: GOTO 3250
3510 REM
3520 REM                Response plots to screen
3530 REM
3540 GOSUB 3890: GOSUB 4120            'Get plot parameters, draw axes
3550 YTOP=0 : YBOT=0 : TIM=T0 : GOSUB 4080
3560 FOR I=0 TO NSAMP
3570   YTOP=YS(I) : YBOT=US(I) : TIM=TSM(I) : GOSUB 4080
3580   CIRCLE(XX,YYT),2
3590   LINE (XP,YP)-(XX,YP)
3600   NEXT I
3610 GOSUB 610 : SCREEN 0 : GOTO 3250
3620 REM
3630 REM                Store results for import to Lotus
3640 REM
3650 CLS : INPUT "Name of storage file (omit extension)";FILENAME$
3660 IF FILENAME$<>"" THEN 3680 ELSE IF FILENAME$="E" OR FILENAME$="e" THEN 3250
3670   PRINT "Please enter a DOS file name or E to Exit" : GOTO 3650
3680 IF LEN(FILENAME$)>8 THEN FILENAME$=LEFT$(FILENAME$,8)
3690 FILEPRN$ = FILENAME$ + ".PRN"
3700 GOSUB 3710: GOSUB 640: GOTO 3250
3710 OPEN "O", #1, FILEPRN$                'Open output file
3720 PRINT #1, Q$;CTYPE$;" PID Algorithm, ";DTYPE$;", ";PTYPE$;Q$
3730 PRINT #1, Q$;"Gain=";Q$;GAIN;Q$;"Tau3=";Q$;TAU3;Q$;"DT=";Q$;DT
3740 PRINT #1, Q$;"Tau1=";Q$;TAU1;Q$;"Tau2=";Q$;TAU2
3750 PRINT #1, Q$;"Kc=";Q$;KC;Q$;"Ti=";Q$;TI;Q$;"Td=";Q$;TD;Q$;"Alpha=";Q$;ALPHA
3760 PRINT #1, Q$;"kw=";Q$;KW;Q$;"Taw3=";Q$;TAW3;Q$;"Rk=";Q$;RK
3770 PRINT #1, Q$;"Taw1=";Q$;TAW1;Q$;"Taw2=";Q$;TAW2
3780 PRINT #1, Q$;"Ts=";Q$;TS;Q$;"IAE=";Q$;IAE
3790 PRINT #1, : PRINT #1, Q$;" Time ";Q$;" ";Q$;"   Y  ";Q$;" ";Q$;"    U   ";Q$
```

```
3800 FOR I=0 TO NSAMP
3810   PRINT #1,TSM(I),YS(I),US(I)
3820   NEXT I
3830 PRINT : PRINT "Results have been stored in file ";FILEPRN$
3840 CLOSE #1 : RETURN
3850 REM
3860 REM                    Output to on-line printer
3870 REM
3880 FILEPRN$="PRN": GOSUB 3710: GOTO 3250
3890 REM
3900 REM         Determine maximum and minimum values for plots
3910 REM
3920 LOCATE 24,30: PRINT "Calculating parameters for the plot
3930 TO=0 : YBMAX = US(0) : YBO = US(0) : YTMAX = YS(0) : YTO = YS(0)
3940 FOR I=1 TO NSAMP
3950   IF YS(I) > YTMAX THEN YTMAX = YS(I)
3960   IF YS(I) < YTO   THEN YTO   = YS(I)
3970   IF US(I) > YBMAX THEN YBMAX = US(I)
3980   IF US(I) < YBO   THEN YBO   = US(I)
3990   NEXT I
4000 YTMAX = YTMAX + .1*(YTMAX - YTO)
4010 YTO   = YTO   - .1*(YTMAX - YTO)
4020 YBMAX = YBMAX + .1*(YBMAX - YBO)
4030 YBO   = YBO   - .1*(YBMAX - YBO)
4040 RETURN
4050 REM
4060 REM         Calculate coordinate of point to be plotted
4070 REM
4080 XP= XX: XX= X0% + (TIM - TO)*(XF% - X0%)/(TMAX-TO)
4090 YP= YY: YY= 220 - Y0% - (YF% - Y0%)*(YBOT - YBO)/(YBMAX-YBO)
4100 YTP= YYT: YYT= 220 - YTO% -(YTF% - YTO%)*(YTOP-YTO)/(YTMAX-YTO)
4110 RETURN
4120 REM         Location parameters for top and bottom plots
4130 CLS
4140 X0%=100: Y0%=130: XF%=600: YF%=210: XTICKS=4: YTICKS=2
4150 GOSUB 4380: YTO%=Y0%: YTF%=YF%                'Draw bottom axes and boxes
4160 Y0%= 50: YF%=130
4170 GOSUB 4380                                    'Draw bottom axes and boxes
4180 RETURN
4190 REM
4200 REM         Subroutine to draw a horizontal axis with xticks
4210 REM
4220 SCREEN 2
4230 LINE -(X0%,220-Y0%),0
4240 DX=(XF% - X0%)/XTICKS
4250 FOR I=1 TO XTICKS
4260   LINE -(X0% + I*DX, 220-Y0%): LINE -STEP(0,-5): LINE -STEP(0,5)
4270   NEXT I: LINE -(X0%,220-Y0%)
4280 RETURN
4290 REM
4300 REM         Subroutine to draw a vertical axis with yticks
4310 REM
4320 LINE -(X0%, 220-Y0%),0
4330 DY = (YF% - Y0%)/YTICKS
4340 FOR I=1 TO YTICKS
4350   LINE -(X0%, 220 - Y0% - I*DY): LINE -STEP(5,0): LINE -STEP(-5,0)
4360   NEXT I: LINE -(X0%, 220-Y0%)
4370 RETURN
4380 REM
4390 REM         Subroutine to draw both axes and a box
4400 REM
4410 GOSUB 4190: GOSUB 4300: LINE (XF%, 220-YF%)-(X0%, 220-Y0%),,B
4420 RETURN
```

Appendix C: Solutions to All Exercises

APPENDIX C

Solutions to All Exercises

Unit 2

Exercise 2-1.

Controlled variable—the speed of the engine.
Manipulated variable—the flow of steam to the engine.
Disturbances—the load (torque) on the main shaft, varying as the various shop machines are started by engaging the clutches.
Sensor—the flywheel governor is the speed sensor.
Block diagram:

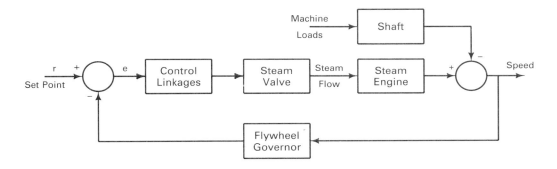

Exercise 2-2.

Controlled variable—the temperature in the oven.
Manipulated variable—electric power to the heating element or gas flow to the burner (operated on/off).
Disturbances—Losses to surroundings, opening the oven door, heat consumed by the cooking process.
Sensor—usually a gas-filled bulb connected to the operating switch through a capillary.
What is varied when the temperature dial is adjusted is the set point.
Block diagram:

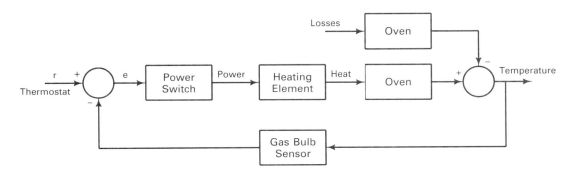

Exercise 2-3.

(a) Change in controller output: 5% × 100/20 = 25%
(b) Change in controller output: 5% × 100/50 = 10%
(c) Change in controller output: 5% × 100/250 = 2%

Exercise 2-4.

Offset in outlet temperature: 8%/(100/20) = 1.6% of range.
In order to eliminate the offset we must open the valve.
Offset for 10% PB: 8%/(100/10) = 0.8% of range.

Exercise 2-5.

For a 5% sustained error, the output of the PI controller will suddenly change by:

$$5\% \times 0.6 = 3\%$$

Then it will increase continuously with time at the rate of:

$$5\% \times 0.6/2 \text{ min} = 1.5\% \text{ per min}$$

The following is a sketch of the controller output response:

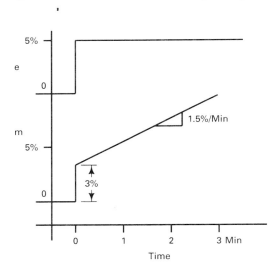

Exercise 2-6.

The output of the PID controller will suddenly change by:

$$5\%/\text{min} \times 1.0 \times 2.0 \text{ min} = 10.0\%$$

Then it will ramp for five minutes at the rate of:

$$5\%/\text{min} \times 1.0 = 5\%/\text{min}$$

After five minutes, the output will suddenly drop by 10.0%, as the error ramp stops. The output will then remain constant at: 5%/min × 5 min × 1.0 = 25%

The following is a sketch of the controller output response:

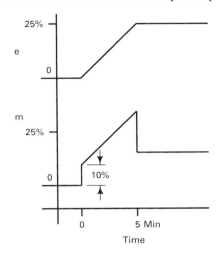

Exercise 2-7.

QDR proportional gain: $1.2 \times 0.45 = 0.54$ or 185% PB
QDR reset rate: $1/(4.5 \text{ min}/1.2) = 0.266$ repeats/min
The tuning formulas are from Table 2-1 for PI controllers.

Exercise 2-8.

Series PID controller:
QDR proportional gain: $1.2 \times 0.6 = 0.72$ or 139% PB
QDR reset rate: $1/(4.5 \text{ min}/2) = 0.444$ repeats/min
QDR derivative time: $4.5 \text{ min}/8 = 0.562$ min
Parallel PID controller:
QDR proportional gain: $1.2 \times 0.75 = 0.90\%/\%$ or 110% PB
QDR reset rate: $1/(4.5 \text{ min}/1.6) = 0.36$ repeats/min
QDR derivative time: $4.5 \text{ min}/10 = 0.45$ min
The tuning formulas are from Table 2-1 for PID controllers.

Unit 3

Exercise 3-1.

a. Put the controller on manual.
b. Change the controller output by a small amount; record the size of the step change and the time at which it is performed.
c. Obtain a recording of the controlled variable versus time.
d. Determine the gain, time constant, and dead time from the response recorded in step c.

Exercise 3-2.

Gain:	The sensitivity of the process output to its input, measured by the steady-state change in output divided by the change in input.
Time Constant:	The response time of the process, determines how long it takes to reach steady state after a disturbance.
Dead Time:	The time it takes for the output to start changing after a disturbance.

Exercise 3-3.

Gain: $K = \dfrac{2\,°F}{100\ lb/h} = 0.02\,°F/(lb/h)$

$= \dfrac{(2\,°F)\ 100/(250 - 200\,°F)}{(100\ lb/h)\ 100/(5000 - 0\ lb/h)} = 2.0\ \%/\%$

Notice that, as the controller output sets the set point of the steam flow controller, the percent of controller output corresponds to the percent of steam flow transmitter output.

Exercise 3-4.

Gain: $K = \dfrac{(84.4 - 90.0)\,°C}{2\ kg/s} = -2.8\,°C/(kg/s)$

Slope method:
    Time constant: 54.8 − 4.7 = 50.1 s (0.84 min)
    Dead time: 4.7 s (0.08 min) (from fig.)
Slope and point method:
    63.2% point: T = 90.0 + 0.632(84.4 − 90.0) = 86.5 °C
                $t_1 = 39.4$ s   (from fig.)
    Time constant: 39.4 − 4.7 = 34.7 s (0.58 min)
    Dead time: 4.7 s (0.08 min) (same as before)

Exercise 3-5.

Two-point method:
    63.2% point is the same as before: $t_1 = 39.4$ s
    28.3% point: T = 90.0 + 0.283(84.4 − 90.0) = 88.4 °C
                $t_2 = 18.3$ s (from fig.)
    Time constant: 1.5(39.4 − 18.3) = 31.6 s (0.53 min)
    Dead time: 39.4 − 31.6 = 7.8 s (0.13 min)

Exercise 3-6.

Maximum time constants:

$$RC = (10 \times 10^6)\ (100 \times 10^{-6}) = 1000\ s$$

Exercise 3-7.

Time constant:

$$A/K_v = (50\ ft^2)/[(50\ gpm/ft)/7.48\ g/ft^3] = 7.48\ min$$

Exercise 3-8.

Product flow:	Time constant:
F = 50 gpm	V/F = 2000/50 = 40.0 min
F = 500 gpm	V/F = 2000/500 = 4.0 min
F = 5000 gpm	V/F = 2000/5000 = 0.4 min

Exercise 3-9.

Steady-state product concentration:

$$[(100)(20) + (400)(2)]/(100 + 400) = 5.60\ lb/gal$$

Product concentration for 10 gpm increase in concentrated solution:

$$[(110)(20) + (400)(2)]/(110 + 400) = 5.88 \text{ lb/gal}$$

Change in product concentration:

$$5.88 - 5.60 = 0.28 \text{ lb/gal}$$

Process gain: $(5.88 - 5.60 \text{ lb/gal})/(110 - 100 \text{ gpm}) = 0.028 \text{ (lb/gal)/gpm}$

Exercise 3-10.

Product concentration:
  Initial: $[(10)(20) + (40)(2)]/(10 + 40) = 5.60 \text{ lb/gal}$
  Final: $[(11)(20) + (40)(2)]/(11 + 40) = 5.88 \text{ lb/gal}$
  Gain: $(5.88 - 5.60)/(11 - 10) = 0.28 \text{ (lb/gal)/gpm}$
Thus, the gain at one tenth throughput is ten times the gain at full throughput.

Unit 4

Exercise 4-1.

If the process gain were to double, the controller gain must be reduced to half its original value to keep the total loop gain constant.

Exercise 4-2.

The loop is less controllable (has a smaller ultimate gain) as the ratio of the process dead time to its time constant increases. The process gain does not affect the controllability of the loop, since the controller gain can be adjusted to maintain a given loop gain.

Exercise 4-3.

The required relationships are:

$$K_{cu} = \frac{2}{K(t_0/\tau)} \qquad T_u = 4t_0$$

Exercise 4-4.

Process A is less sensitive to changes in controller output than processes B and C, which have equal sensitivity. Process C is more controllable than processes A and B, which are equally controllable.
Process A has the fastest response of the three, and process C the slowest.

Exercise 4-5.

Quarter-decay tuning formulas for series PID controller, from the formulas on Table 4-1:

	Process A	Process B	Process C
Uncontrollability	0.5	0.5	0.2
Gain, %/%	4.8	1.2	3.0
Reset time, min	0.17	3.0	4.0
Derivative, min	0.04	0.75	1.0

Exercise 4-6.

To adjust for 8 s sample time we must add $8/2 = 4$ s (0.067 min) to the process dead time. Once more, from the formulas of Table 4-1:

	Process A	Process B	Process C
Uncontrollability	0.9	0.52	0.21
Gain, %/%	2.7	1.15	2.90
Reset time, min	0.3	3.13	4.13
Derivative, min	0.08	0.78	1.03

Exercise 4-7.

The tuning parameters for minimum IAE on disturbance inputs, from the formulas of Table 4-2, for the parallel PID controller.

	Process A	Process B	Process C
Gain, %/%	5.4	1.4	3.2
Reset time, min	0.1	2.0	3.4
Derivative, min	0.04	0.66	0.77

Exercise 4-8.

The tuning parameters for minimum IAE on set point changes, from the formulas of Table 4-5, for the parallel PID controller:

	Process A	Process B	Process C
Gain, %/%	4.0	1.0	2.2
Reset time, min	0.25	4.4	14.0
Derivative, min	0.03	0.55	0.8

Exercise 4-9.

The minimum IAE criteria on set point changes is preferred for the slave controller in a cascade system because it produces fast response with about 5% overshoot. The disturbance and quarter-decay formulas are too oscillatory on set point changes for a slave controller.

Unit 5

Exercise 5-1.

Tight level control is indicated when the level has significant effect on the process operation, as in a natural-circulation evaporator or reboiler. Averaging level control is to be used when it is necessary to smooth out sudden variations in flow, as in a surge tank receiving discharge from batch operations to feed a continuous process. The tight level control is the one that requires the level to be kept at or very near its set point.

Exercise 5-2.

Controller synthesis consists of deriving the controller transfer function required to meet a specified closed-loop response and compensate for a given process transfer function. Perfect feedback control is not possible because the controller must act on an error; that is, the error cannot be zero at all times.

Exercise 5-3.

The performance parameter in Dahlin's specification is the closed-loop time constant. It can be used to balance rapid elimination of the error with reasonable variation of the controller output. Of the three controller tuning parameters, only the gain is affected by the performance parameter.

Exercise 5-4.

The series PID controller results from the synthesis procedure when the process model is:
1. A second-order system. In this case the integral time is set equal to the longest time constant, and the derivative time equal to the smallest time constant.
2. A first-order plus dead time system. In this case the integral time is set equal to the process time constant and the derivative time equal to half the process dead time.

Exercise 5-5.

Controller synthesis results in a proportional-derivative (PD) controller for an integrating process. Disturbance inputs cause offset, but set point changes do not.

Exercise 5-6.

A pure integral controller is synthesized for a very fast process, modeled by a simple gain.

Exercise 5-7.

For flow control loops synthesis recommends a pure integral controller if the controller is stand-alone, or proportional-integral (PI) if the controller is the slave of a cascade control loop.

Exercise 5-8.

Tuning comparison for quarter-decay ratio (QDR, Table 4-1), minimum IAE on disturbances (Table 4-2), minimum IAE on set point (Table 4-5), and synthesis (Eq. 5-20):

		QDR	Min. IAE Dist.	Min. IAE Set Point	Synth. $\tau_c = 0$
(a)	$t_0 = 0.01$ min				
	Gain, %/%	120	100	59.4	100
	Reset time, min	0.02	0.04	1.4	1.0
	Derivative, min	0.005	0.003	0.005	0.005
(b)	$t_0 = 0.3$ min				
	Gain, %/%	4.0	4.3	3.1	3.3
	Reset time, min	0.6	0.5	1.4	1.0
	Derivative, min	0.15	0.12	0.12	0.15
(c)	$t_0 = 2.0$ min				
	Gain, %/%	0.6	0.8	0.6	0.5
	Reset time, min	4.0	1.9	2.1	1.0
	Derivative, min	1.0	1.1	0.66	1.0

Exercise 5-9.

The typical symptom of reset windup is excessive overshoot of the controlled variable; it is caused by saturation of the controller output beyond the limits of the manipulated variable. Reset windup can be prevented in simple feedback loops by limiting the controller output at points that coincide with the limits of the manipulated variable.

Unit 6

Exercise 6-1.

The velocity algorithm is (1) easier to initialize and (2) easier to limit than the position algorithm.

Exercise 6-2.

The "derivative kick" is a pulse on the controller output that takes place at the next sample after the set point is changed and lasts for one sample. It can be prevented by having the derivative term act on the process variable instead of on the error.

The derivative filter or "dynamic gain limit" is needed to prevent large amplification of changes in the process variable when the derivative time is much longer than the algorithm sample time.

Exercise 6-3.

The "proportional kick" is a large step change in controller output right after a set point change; it can be eliminated by having the proportional term act on the process variable instead of on the error, so that the operator can apply large changes in set point without danger of upsetting the process. When the proportional kick is avoided, the process variable approaches the set point slowly after it is changed, at a rate determined by the integral time. Whenever it is necessary to have the process variable follow set point changes fast, as in the slave controller of a cascade system, the proportional kick must not be avoided.

Exercise 6-4.

All three tuning parameters of the parallel version of the PID algorithm are different from the parameters for the series version. The difference is minor if the derivative time is much smaller than the integral time.

Exercise 6-5.

The nonlinear gain allows the proportional band to be wider than 100% when the error is near zero, which is equivalent to having a larger tank in an averaging level control situation. To have a gain of 0.25%/% (400% PB) at zero error, the nonlinear gain must be:

$$[(1/0.25) - 1]/50 = 0.06 \ (\%/\%)/\% \text{ error}$$

This calculation assumes a proportional-only controller with a bias term of 50% and a set point of 50%.

Exercise 6-6.

Using the formulas of Table 6-1, with q = 0 (for maximum gain) and the following parameters:

$$K = 1.6\%/\% \quad \tau_1 = 10 \text{ min} \quad \tau_2 = 0 \quad t_0 = 2.5 \text{ min}$$

Sample time, min	0.067	1	10	50
$a_1 = \exp(-T/\tau_1)$	0.9934	0.905	0.368	0.0067
$a_2 = \exp(-T/\tau_2)$	0	0	0	0
$N = t_0/T$	37	2	0	0
Controller gain, %/%	2.5	2.0	0.4	0.004
Integral time, min	10.0	9.5	5.8	0.34
Derivative time, min	0	0	0	0

Exercise 6-7.

If the algorithm has dead time compensation, the gain can be higher because it does not have to be adjusted for dead time. This only affects the first two cases, because the dead time is less than one sample for cases (c) and (d), and, therefore, no dead time compensation is necessary. From Eq. (6-14) and Table 6-1:

Sample time, min	0.067	1
Samples of dead time compensation	37	2
Gain, %/%	93	5.9
Integral time, min	10	9.5

Exercise 6-8.

The basic idea of the Smith Predictor is to bypass the process dead time to make the loop more controllable. This is accomplished with an internal model of the process responding to the manipulated variable in parallel with the process. The basic disadvantage is that a complete process model is required, but it is not used to tune the controller, creating too many adjustable parameters.

The Dahlin Algorithm produces the same dead time compensation as the Smith Predictor, but it uses the model to tune the controller, reducing the number of adjustable parameters to one, q.

Unit 7

Exercise 7-1.

Cascade control (1) takes care of disturbances into the slave loop, reducing their effect on the controlled variable; (2) makes the master loop more controllable by speeding up the inner part of the process; and (3) handles the nonlinearities in the inner loop where they have less effect on controllability.

Exercise 7-2.

For cascade control to improve the control performance, the inner loop must be faster than the outer loop. The sensor of the slave loop must be reliable and fast, although it does not have to be accurate.

Exercise 7-3.

The master controller in a slave control system has the same requirements as the controller in a simple feedback control loop; thus, the tuning and mode selection of the master controller are no different from those for a single controller.

Exercise 7-4.

The tuning of the slave controller is different because it has to respond to constant set point changes, which it must follow quickly without too much oscillation. The slave controller should not have integral mode when its presence would limit the proportional gain of the slave controller. If the slave is to have derivative mode, it must act on the process variable so that it is not in series with the derivative mode of the master controller.

Exercise 7-5.

The controllers in a cascade system must be tuned from the inside out, because each slave controller forms part of the process controlled by the master around it.

Exercise 7-6.

Temperature as the slave variable (1) introduces a lag because of the sensor lag, and (2) may cause reset windup because its range of operation is narrower than the transmitter range. These difficulties can be handled by (1) using derivative on the process variable to compensate for the sensor lag, and (2) having the slave measurement fed to the master controller as its reset feedback variable.

Exercise 7-7.

Pressure is a good slave variable because its measurement is fast and reliable. The major difficulties are (1) that the operating range may be narrower than the transmitter range, and (2) that part of the operating range may be outside the transmitter range, e.g., vacuum when the transmitter range includes only positive gage pressures.

Exercise 7-8.

In a computer cascade control system the slave controller must be processed more frequently than the master controller.

Exercise 7-9.

Reset windup can occur in cascade control when the operating range of the slave variable is wider than the transmitter range. To prevent it, the slave measurement can be passed to the reset feedback of the master; in such a scheme the master always takes action based on the current measurement, not on its set point.

Unit 8

Exercise 8-1.

A feedback controller acts on the error. Thus, if there were no error, there would be no control action. In theory, perfect control is possible with feedforward control, but it requires perfect process modeling and compensation.

Exercise 8-2.

To be used by itself, feedforward control requires that all the disturbances be measured as well as accurate models of how the disturbances and the manipulated variable affect the controlled variable.

Feedforward with feedback trim has the advantages that only the major disturbances have to be measured and compensation does not have to be exact, because the integral action of the feedback controller takes care of the minor disturbance and the model error.

Exercise 8-3.

Ratio control consists of making the set point of the manipulated flow proportional to the measurement of a varying flow. It is the simplest form of feedforward control.

For the air-to-natural gas ratio controller of Fig. 7-5:
Control objective: Maintain constant the nitrogen-to-hydrogen ratio of the fresh synthesis gas.
Measured disturbance: Natural gas flow (production rate).
Manipulated variable: The set point of the air flow controller.

Exercise 8-4.

A lead-lag unit is a linear dynamic compensator consisting of a lead (a proportional plus derivative term) and a lag (a low-pass filter), each having an adjustable time constant. It is used in feedforward control to advance or delay the compensation so as to dynamically match the effect of the disturbance.

The step response of a lead-lag unit is an immediate step of amplitude proportional to the lead-to-lag ratio, followed by an exponential approach to the steady-state compensation at a rate controlled by the lag time constant.

The response of a lead-lag unit to a ramp is a ramp that leads the input ramp by the difference between the lead and the lag time constants, or lags it by the difference between the lag and the lead time constants.

Exercise 8-5.

To lead by 1.5 minutes with amplification of 2:

$$1.5 \text{ min} = \text{lead} - \text{lag} = 2(\text{lag}) - \text{lag} = \text{lag}$$

Therefore, a lag of 1.5 minutes and a lead of 3.0 minutes.

Exercise 8-6.

Dead time compensation consists of storing the feedforward compensation and playing it back some time later. The time delay is the adjustable dead time parameter.

Dead time compensation can be used only when the feedforward action is to be delayed and a computer or microprocessor device is available to implement it. It should be used only when the delay time is long relative to the process time constant.

Exercise 8-7.

Design of a feedforward controller for process furnace:
1. Control objective: $T_o = T_o^{set}$
2. Measured disturbances: W, process flow, lb/h
   F_s, supp. fuel flow, scfh
   T_i, inlet process temp., °F
3. Manipulated variable: F^{set}, main fuel flow, gph
4. Steady-state energy balance on furnace:

$$(F\Delta H_m + F_s\Delta H_s)Eff = WC(T_o - T_i)$$

where ΔH_m is the heating value of the main fuel in Btu/gal, ΔH_s is that of the supplementary fuel gas in Btu/scf, Eff is the efficiency of the furnace, and C is the specific heat of the process fluid in Btu/lb-°F.

Solve for the manipulated variable and substitute the control objective:

$$F^{set} = (C/Eff\Delta H_m)\ (T_o^{set} - T_i)W - (\Delta H_s/\Delta H_m)F_s$$

5. Numerical values are needed to evaluate the importance of each disturbance. The change in each disturbance required to cause a given change in main fuel flow would be calculated.
6. Feedback trim can be added as in Example 8-1:
   Feedback output: $m = CT_o^{set}/(Eff\Delta H_m)$
   Design formula:

$$F^{set} = [m - (C/Eff\Delta H_m)T_i]W - (\Delta H_s/\Delta H_m)F_s$$

7. Lead-lag units must be installed on the process flow and inlet temperatures, but not on the supplementary fuel gas flow, because its dynamic effect should match that of the main fuel gas flow.
8. Instrumentation diagram:

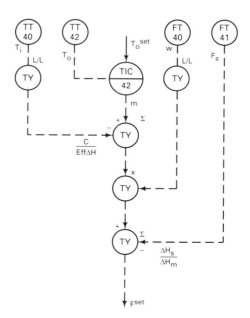

Unit 9

Exercise 9-1.

Loop interaction takes place when the manipulated variable of each loop affects the controlled variable of the other loop. The effect is that the gain and the dynamic response of each loop change when the auto/manual state or tuning of the other loops change.

When loop interaction is present, we can (1) pair the loops in the way that minimizes the effect of interaction and (2) design a control scheme that decouples the loops.

Exercise 9-2.

Open-loop gain of a loop is the change in its controlled variable divided by the change in its manipulated variable when all other loops are opened (in manual).

Closed-loop gain is the gain of a loop when all other loops are closed (auto state) and have integral mode.

Relative gain (interaction measure) for a loop is the ratio of its open-loop gain to its closed-loop gain.

Exercise 9-3.

To minimize interaction for a loop, the relative gain for that loop must be as close to unity as possible. Thus, the loops must be paired to keep the relative gains close to unity, which, in a system with more than two control objectives, will require ranking the objectives.

The relative gains are easy to determine because they involve only a steady-state model of the process, which is usually available at design time.

The main drawback of the relative gain is that it does not take into account the dynamic response of the loops.

Exercise 9-4.

When all four relative gains are 0.5, the effect of interaction is the same for both pairing options. The gain of each loop will double when the other loop is switched to automatic. The interaction is positive; that is, the loops help each other.

Exercise 9-5.

When the effect of interaction with other loops is in the same direction as the direct effect for that loop, the interaction is positive; if the interaction and direct effects are in opposite direction, the interaction is negative. For positive interaction, the relative gain is positive and less than unity, while for negative interaction the relative gain is either negative or greater than unity.

Exercise 9-6.

Interaction for top composition to reflux and bottom composition to steam:
$$(0.05)(0.05)/[(0.05)(0.05) - (-0.02)(-0.02)] = 1.19$$

Relative gains:

	Reflux	Steam
Y_d	1.19	-0.19
X_b	-0.19	1.19

The top composition must be paired to the reflux and the bottom composition to the steam to minimize the effect of interaction.

Exercise 9-7.

Let H be the flow of the hot water in gpm, C the flow of the cold water in gpm, F the total flow in gpm, and T the shower temperature in °F. The mass and energy balances on the shower, neglecting variations in density and specific heat, give the following formulas:

$$F = H + C \qquad T = (170H + 80C)/(H + C)$$

These are the same formulas as for the blender of Example 9-2. So, the relative gains are:

	Hot	Cold
$\cdot$ F	H/F	C/F
T	C/F	H/F

For the numbers in the problem:

$$H = (3 \text{ gpm})(110 - 80)/(170 - 80) = 1 \text{ gpm} \qquad C = 2 \text{ gpm}$$

So, as the cold water flow is the higher, use it to control the flow, and use the hot water flow to control the temperature. The relative gain for this pairing is:

$$C/F = 2/3 = 0.67$$

The gain of each loop increases by 50% when the other loop is closed.

Exercise 9-8.

As in the second part of Example 9-4, we can use a ratio controller to maintain a constant temperature when the flow changes. We would then ratio the hot water flow (smaller) to the cold water flow (larger) and manipulate the cold water flow to control the total flow. The design ratio is 0.5 gpm of hot water per gpm of cold water.

Unit 10

Exercise 10-1.

When the process dynamic characteristics (gain, time constant, and dead time) are expected to change significantly over the region of operation, adaptive control is worthwhile to maintain the control loop performance. Most loops can be controlled satisfactorily without adaptive control, because either their characteristics do not vary much or their controllability is high and insensitive to variation in the process dynamic parameters.

Exercise 10-2.

The process parameter most likely to change and affect the control loop performance is the process gain. An example of extreme variation in process gain is the control of pH in the water neutralization process.

Exercise 10-3.

The equal percentage valve characteristic compensates for the decrease in process gain with increasing throughput, typical of many blending, heat transfer, and separation processes. For the equal percentage characteristic to properly compensate for gain variations: (1) the pressure drop across the valve must remain constant, (2) the controller output must actuate the valve (it must not be cascaded to a flow controller), (3) the valve must not operate in the lower 5% of its range, where the characteristic deviates from equal percentage.

Exercise 10-4.

When a feedback controller adjusts the ratio of a ratio controller, its output is multiplied by the process flow, directly compensating for the gain decrease with throughput.

Exercise 10-5.

A gap or dead band controller can be used for a "valve position controller" that adjusts a large reagent valve in parallel with a small valve to maintain the small valve position near half opened. This way the large valve makes rough adjustments in flow but does not move when the small valve is doing fine adjustments near neutrality, where the process gain is highest.

Exercise 10-6.

A pattern recognition controller matches an underdamped response curve to the response of the error by detecting the peaks of the response. The decay ratio is then controlled by adjusting the controller gain, and the oscillation period is used to adjust the integral and derivative times.

Exercise 10-7.

The second-order discrete model matches the sampled response of most processes, because its form is the same for monotonic, oscillatory, inverse response, integrating, and unstable responses.

The parameters of a discrete model, except for the dead time, can be estimated using least squares regression techniques. The second-order model requires only six parameters, including a bias term to account for disturbances.

Exercise 10-8.

For least squares regression to successfully estimate the dynamic process model parameters, (1) the process variable must be changing due to changes in the controller output, (2) the input/output data must be differenced or at least entered as differences from their initial steady-state values, and (3) the noise on the process variable must not be autocorrelated.

Exercise 10-9.

Recursive estimation provides estimates of the parameters that improve with each sample of the process input and output. It is convenient to do on-line autotuning and the only way to do adaptive control. To use recursive regression for autotuning, the process driving function and initial covariance matrix are set, and an estimation run is made with the forgetting factor set to unity. In adaptive control the estimator is kept running with the forgetting factor set at a value less than unity.

Exercise 10-10.

The diagonal terms of the variance-covariance matrix are the multipliers of the variance of the noise to obtain the variance of the corresponding estimated parameters. To keep a parameter from changing during estimation, the corresponding initial diagonal value of the variance-covariance matrix is set to zero.

Index

Index